D1587189

Given to the

BRITISH MUSEUM
CENTRAL LIBRARY

WITHDRAWN

by ___ARS ARTIS___

___AUGUST, 2004___

*Chinese Ceramics, Bronzes and Jades
in the collection of
Sir Alan and Lady Barlow*

by the same author

*

AN INTRODUCTION TO CHINESE ART
CHINESE ART IN THE TWENTIETH CENTURY

A. Pair of serving girls. Pottery, slipped, painted and glazed. Ht. $10\frac{1}{4}''$ and $10\frac{1}{2}''$. T'ang Dynasty, VII century. (S.3, page 21)

CHINESE CERAMICS BRONZES AND JADES

in the collection of

SIR ALAN AND LADY BARLOW

by

MICHAEL SULLIVAN

FABER AND FABER LIMITED
24 RUSSELL SQUARE · LONDON

First published in mcmlxiii
by Faber and Faber Limited
24 Russell Square London W.C.1
Printed in Great Britain by
R. MacLehose and Company Limited
The University Press Glasgow

Contents

7

Colour Plates

Maps

Chronological Table

SHANG-YIN   B.C. *c.* **1600–c.1030**

CHOU
- Western Chou — *c.* 1030– 722
- 'Spring and Autumn' Period — 722– 481
- Warring States — *c.* 481– 221

CHOU *c.* **1030– 256**

CH'IN   **221– 207**

HAN
- Former (Western Han) — B.C. 202– 9 A.D.
- Hsin — 9– 23
- Later (Eastern) Han — 25–221

HAN B.C. **202– 220** A.D.

THREE KINGDOMS
- Shu (Han) — 221–263
- Wei — 220–265
- Wu — 222–280

THREE KINGDOMS **221– 265**

SOUTHERN (Six Dynasties)
- Chin — 265–316
- Eastern Chin — 317–420
- Liu Sung — 420–479
- Southern Ch'i — 479–502
- Liang — 502–557
- Ch'en — 557–587

and

NORTHERN DYNASTIES
- Northern Wei (T'o-pa) — 386–535
- Eastern Wei (T'o-pa) — 534–543
- Western Wei (T'o-pa) — 535–554
- Northern Ch'i — 550–577
- Northern Chou (Hsien-pi) — 557–581

SOUTHERN and NORTHERN DYNASTIES **265– 581**

SUI   **581– 618**

T'ANG   **618– 906**

FIVE DYNASTIES
- Later Liang — 907–922
- Later T'ang (Turkic) — 923–936
- Later Chin (Turkic) — 936–948
- Later Han (Turkic) — 946–950
- Later Chou — 951–960

FIVE DYNASTIES **907– 960**

Liao (Khitan Tartars) — 907–1125

Hsi-hsia (Tangut Tibetan) — 990–1227

SUNG
- Northern Sung — 960–1126
- Southern Sung — 1127–1279

SUNG **960–1279**

Chin (Jurchen Tartars) — 1115–1234

YÜAN (Mongols)   **1260–1368**

10

CHRONOLOGICAL TABLE

MING	Hung-wu	1368–1398	**1368–1644**
	Chien-wen	1399–1402	
	Yung-lo	1403–1424	
	Hung-hsi	1425	
	Hsüan-te	1426–1435	
	Cheng-t'ung	1436–1449	
	Ching-t'ai	1450–1457	
	T'ien-shun	1457–1464	
	Ch'eng-hua	1465–1487	
	Hung-chih	1488–1505	
	Cheng-te	1506–1521	
	Chia-ching	1522–1566	
	Lung-ch'ing	1567–1572	
	Wan-li	1573–1620	
	T'ai-ch'ang	1620	
	T'ien-ch'i	1621–1627	
	Ch'ung-chen	1628–1644	
CH'ING (Manchu)	Shun-chih	1644–1661	**1644–1912**
	K'ang-hsi	1662–1722	
	Yung-cheng	1723–1735	
	Ch'ien-lung	1736–1795	
	Chia-ch'ing	1796–1821	
	Tao-kuang	1821–1850	
	Hsien-feng	1851–1861	
	T'ung-chih	1862–1873	
	Kuang-hsü	1874–1908	
	Hsüan-t'ung	1909–1912	
REPUBLIC			**1912–**

11

Introduction

Sir Alan Barlow began collecting when he was an undergraduate at Oxford. He used a prize which he had won to make his first purchase, a Persian bowl. From this modest beginning he built up over the years an important collection of Persian pottery which he and Lady Barlow later presented to the Ashmolean Museum. His love of ceramics brought him, in the early 'twenties, into contact with George Eumorfopoulos, Oscar Raphael and other notable collectors whose interests were mainly Chinese. He joined their intimate circle, saw, and was conquered. In 1922 he bought his first Chinese piece, and from that moment, as he puts it, 'never looked back'. In 1933 he joined the Council of the Oriental Ceramic Society, and ten years later became its President, an office he has held for eighteen years. 'For the whole of that period', wrote Sir Harry Garner on Sir Alan's retirement in December 1961, 'his wise guidance and generous help have been of inestimable value to the Society and its present high reputation is due, very largely, to his influence.'

Collectors often develop their taste through successive phases, first buying late and decorative pieces of obvious appeal and minor importance, then turning perhaps to the earlier wares, gradually refining their choice and increasing their knowledge till, having built up a reputable collection, they are only too glad to forget their early indiscretions. Sir Alan Barlow knew what he wanted from the start, and his first purchase set the key for thirty years of collecting of remarkable consistency. His interest in ceramics begins with the Six Dynasties and ends with the Ming, and so covers the periods in the history of the art in China when form was at its simplest and most robust, when colour was warm and restrained, and decoration subordinated to shape. The brilliant techniques and lifeless perfection of the later wares hold no appeal for him, nor has he ever been attracted by mere rarity.

The collection is most notable for its splendid range of T'ang wares, and for a group of celadons in which we may trace the whole history of that important Chekiang family from its earliest beginnings in the Yüeh ware of the third century A.D. up to the Ming Dynasty. The classic Ting and Chün are well represented; there is a lively group of Tz'u-chou wares, and a lovely collection of *ch'ing-pai*, while almost the full range of black wares, Northern and Southern, is included. The single piece of Ju, one of the very few in private hands in the West, seems in its restrained perfection of form and colour to typify the quality of the collection as a whole.

The part of the collection that is probably best known is the tomb figurines. There are notable examples of both Six Dynasties and T'ang date, unglazed, glazed, and painted. The famous 'tired horse', S. 25 (Pl. 9a) is surely one of the most sensitively-modelled T'ang figurines in existence, while no one could fail to surrender to the charm of the pair of girl attendants (Colour Pl. A), one of whom carries in her hands, as though in symbolic offering to its owner, a miniature replica of the first Chinese piece Sir Alan ever bought.

13

INTRODUCTION

The collection contains a group of archaic bronzes, small in number but high in quality, of the Late Shang and Early Chou Dynasties, the Warring States, Han and T'ang. Several are inscribed, and they are distinguished, like all the collection, less for their archaeological interest than for their beauty of shape, decoration and patina. The T'ang mirror with repoussé dragons in silver and silver-gilt on a bed of lacquer is unique in Western collections.

The jades take their place in about the proportion in which we would find them in the library of a Chinese gentleman-scholar. Among the pieces one would single out are the belt-ring, the *pi*-disc, a cousin of the famous disc in Kansas City, and the splendid water-vessel in the form of a winged feline monster. Here again it is the restrained beauty of material and form rather than technical cleverness or archaeological value that distinguishes these pieces.

The collection contains only one example of Chinese stone sculpture, the seated lion illustrated in Pl. 14; but it is a piece of outstanding beauty.

When, in 1961, Sir Alan retired from the Presidency of the Oriental Ceramic Society, the Council of the Society decided, as a measure of their deep regard for him, to republish a paper he had read to the Society in April 1937, entitled 'The Collector and the Expert', and to present him with a bound copy of it on his eightieth birthday. In this paper, Sir Alan posed a question which must be, or ought to be, in the minds of all collectors from time to time : Is the collector any use? What justification is there for his acquisitiveness? To this he answered, 'I would suggest that he can be forgiven — indeed can only be forgiven — for being acquisitive if he is also inquisitive, that a measure of hoarding is only pardonable if it leads, not merely to the development in the individual of knowledge, but to its dissemination.' And he went on to say, 'The collector ought to take risks. If he boasts that he has never acquired an object, the authenticity of which was subsequently disproved, we should surely admire his judgement or his caution less than we deplored his poorness of spirit.'

When selecting pieces for inclusion in this Catalogue, we found barely half a dozen out of nearly four hundred the authenticity of which, if not disproved, was at least open to question. Characteristically, Sir Alan readily agreed that it would be of value to other collectors if these were included also. We have accordingly put them in a special section entitled 'Problem Pieces', in company with others the antiquity of which is not in doubt, but to which we are unable, in the present state of our knowledge, to attach any definite labels.

'The Collector and the Expert' was written at a time when the industrial arts in Great Britain were just beginning to emerge from the century-long chaos bequeathed by the Industrial Revolution. Sir Alan suggested that the forming of a collection of Chinese ceramics might be further justified if it contributed to the raising of standards of taste. Since then, Chinese wares, and particularly the Sung wares in which this collection is so rich, have indeed had a profound influence not only upon the ceramics industry but also upon individual potters in Britain, and there can be little doubt that this collection, which its owners show so readily and lend so generously, has played its part in this revolution in taste.[1]

[1] For example, twenty-two pieces from the Barlow Collection were shown at the International Exhibition of Chinese Art at Burlington House in 1935–36, while no less than sixty were lent for a long period of study and display to the White Wares Study Group formed by the Oriental Ceramic Society in 1961–62. Sir Alan

INTRODUCTION

In one sense, this Catalogue has been written at an inopportune moment in the study of Chinese ceramics. In the years when many of these pieces were acquired, it was still possible to adhere fairly closely to what John Pope has called the 'one ware, one kiln philosophy'. But under the impact of twelve years of discovery and excavation in China, and of intensive research in Japan and in the West, this approach to the identification of Chinese ceramics has been undermined. We have tried in the notes that preface most of the sections to give, if only in outline, the most important information that has recently come to light. This new material does not always make it easier to identify an individual piece — indeed, it may make it more difficult — but it will at least suggest to the reader the extent to which recent discoveries have complicated a once simple picture of the development of Chinese ceramics.

One of the problems these discoveries have posed is that of nomenclature. It is now well established, for example, that 'Tz'u-chou ware' was made at many factories in North China besides Tz'u-chou. Some writers consequently are in favour of dropping the name altogether, and substituting for it some such term as 'North China painted stoneware', or 'North China popular ware'. The former, however, is too inaccurate, and the latter too vague, to be of much value. It would seem better to acknowledge that Tz'u-chou, like Yangshao or Swatow, has come to denote a whole class of wares the general characteristics of which are readily recognized, and within that class to distinguish the particular kiln where possible. This is the procedure we have followed here. Another difficulty concerns the description of the body. It is customary, for example, to describe nearly all celadons as porcelain. They are, however, more often a porcellanous stoneware, and in general we have reserved the word 'porcelain' for wares having a white, vitreous and translucent body. But some inconsistency is unavoidable.

As each piece was acquired, Sir Alan Barlow added to his index a fresh card on which he subsequently jotted down the opinions of amateurs and experts who over the years visited Boswells and studied the collection. We have found their—often conflicting—comments both suggestive and stimulating,[1] and we would like to record our thanks to them and at the same time to assure them that they have not been quoted. I would also like to take this opportunity to thank Arthur Lane and Sir Harry Garner for their suggestions, the former on some of the pieces in the collection, the latter on sections of the text; to Sir Harry, and through him to the Oriental Ceramic Society, are also due our thanks for the loan of illustrations which have appeared in the Transactions of the Society. The photographs on Plate 144 were very kindly provided by Lieut.-Col. W. B. R. Neave-Hill and Mr. Paul Toller, the Chinese characters on page 157 written by Mr. Lee Yim of the School of Oriental and African Studies. The maps were drawn by Mr. N. S. Hyslop. Finally, I should like to thank Miss Daphne Martin of Messrs. Faber and Faber for the care with which she has seen the book through the press.

and Lady Barlow have also contributed to all the relevant OCS exhibitions in London, and have lent pieces to important exhibitions in France, Italy, Canada and the United States. An exhibition of sixty-nine masterpieces from the collection was held at the Arts Council galleries in London in 1953.

[1] Excepting perhaps the verdict of one world-renowned authority on one of the figurines, 'Dubious, but probably authentic'. Was it this, one wonders, that prompted Sir Alan's wry comments on scholarly opinions in 'The Collector and the Expert'?

INTRODUCTION

In the preparation of this Catalogue, my wife Khoan and I have worked together at every stage. While the responsibility for its contents is wholly mine, she has brought to it the virtues of an orderly mind and a sensitive and unclouded eye; she has done valuable work on recent Chinese sources, and has taken entirely upon her own shoulders the only arduous part of the work, that of standardizing the individual entries and of typing the manuscript.

To the pleasure of this partnership has been added our delight in the collection and its owners. There was surely never a collector so acute and open-minded in receiving the opinions of all who have come to share his love of his pots. And none so genial and warm-hearted as Lady Barlow, through whose house and beautiful garden life flows in an endless stream of visitors, while she responds equally to the claims of Darwinists and devoted grandchildren. We would like to record our thanks to the Barlows for making our task so enjoyable, and our regret that the day had to come when it was finished.

M.S.

1. Figurines

The custom in China of placing figurines in the tomb is at least as old as the Shang Dynasty. A pottery figure of a prisoner with his hands manacled, found in a grave at Anyang, was presumably intended as a substitute for a human sacrifice. Six hundred years later Confucius, in a celebrated passage, rebuked the man who had first thought of putting straw figures in the tomb, which, he wrongly supposed, had led to the inhuman custom of immolation, still occasionally practised in his time. These straw figures have of course all perished, but many of the wooden figures used by the Ch'u people of Central China during the Warring States have recently been excavated, miraculously preserved in the water-logged soil of Changsha.

The purpose of these figures was to serve, or protect, the spirit of the departed; this indeed applied to all the objects placed in the grave, which were together classed as *ming-ch'i* (literally 'spirit utensils'). However, an inscription, recorded by Wang Kuo-wei, on a Han model of a cooking stove, suggests that the mourning relatives who placed it in the tomb were as much concerned for their own future as for that of the deceased. 'He who uses this stove,' it runs, 'may his descendants be rich and honourable, and happy without end . . . and have long life without misfortune.'

In the Han Dynasty, more care was lavished on the tomb and its contents than ever before or since. 'In the Capital', wrote the Han poet Wang Fu, 'the royal kinsmen, and in the provinces and districts the powerful families, neglect their aged in life, and give them magnificent funerals in death; large quantities of precious things are buried with them — figures of people, horses and carriages. . . .' These practices were continued, with little change, during the Six Dynasties.

Under the T'ang, strict regulations were enforced laying down the size and number of the figures that might be placed in the tomb. Officials of the third rank and above, for example, were allowed ninety kinds; those of the fourth and fifth ranks, seventy; those from the sixth to the ninth rank, forty. The dress and ornaments of the figurines, moreover, had to conform to their rank when living. They are consequently a valuable source of information on ancient costume and insignia, while the houses and farms, cooking stoves, herdsmen and pigsties, give us a vivid picture of the rural and domestic economy of ancient China.

The Han figures are either unglazed, painted, or coloured with a green lead glaze to which time and decomposition have lent a silvery iridescence. During the Six Dynasties, glazing was much less common and the characteristic dark clay was generally either painted or left plain. The last years of the sixth century saw the introduction of whitish porcelain covered with a creamy, finely crackled glaze, followed in the seventh century by the rich polychrome glazes which we consider typically T'ang. The cobalt glaze was probably introduced, from Western Asia, late in the seventh or early in the eighth century.[1]

---

[1] A camel bearing a five-man orchestra on his back and decorated with polychrome glazes, including cobalt, was excavated recently from a tomb dated 723 in Sian. It is reproduced in my *Introduction to Chinese Art* (London, 1959), Pl. 85.

FIGURINES

Generally, however, the exposed skin of the T'ang figurines is unglazed and given a flesh-tinted slip, with the features delicately painted in.

Under the T'ang, the modelling and glazing become more and more sumptuous, reaching their climax during the brilliant K'ai-yüan era (713–42). So grand, indeed, had burials become by the end of this period that it was necessary to introduce regulations forbidding the use of gold, silver, bronze or pewter in the tomb. These sumptuary laws, combined with the fall in the living standards which followed the disastrous An Lu-shan rebellion of 756, brought about a decline in quality. It seems likely that a comparatively larger proportion of the glazed figures of the type of the woman feeding a parakeet (Pl. 11b) were made shortly before the middle of the century, whereas the majority of unglazed figures in the same style, such as Pl. 13a, were made after 750. This is not an infallible guide, however. Recently published finds from tombs in Shensi include many unglazed early T'ang figures; but there are few glazed ones that can be dated after 750 with any certainty. It seems that the sumptuary regulations were less enforced, or enforceable, in areas far from the capital. In Szechwan, for example, potters continued to make T'ang-style figures with polychrome glazes well into the Sung Dynasty.

Among the notable figurines in this collection are the seated camel bearing a bearded Westerner on his back (Pl. 4a), and the compact figure, delightfully, but quite inexplicably, labelled 'the sleeping gardener' (Pl. 5b); he must surely be a camel-boy, sunk in exhausted sleep at the end of a long day's march across the desert — a sight the Chinese potter must often have seen at the gates of Changan. The barking watch-dog (Pl. 4b), the most popular piece, judging from the number of postcards sold, at Burlington House in 1935, is a wonderfully lively piece of modelling; while in quieter mood, the oft-exhibited 'tired horse' (Pl. 9a) is among the most sensitively realized of all T'ang figurines. A rather unusual figure is the young girl on the camel (Pl. 5a); her features are Chinese, but her dress is foreign — perhaps a Chinese returning to her homeland from Central Asia. The pair of exquisite cream-glazed serving girls (early T'ang), modelled with the delicate charm of French mediaeval ivories, are of particular interest because one of them (Colour Pl. A) bears in her hands a miniature replica of the covered jar in this collection, Pl. 26a.

In quite another period and ceramic tradition, the white porcelain Kuanyin (Pl. 15) must surely be one of the most perfect specimens of its kind.

S. 23   Pl. 1a
Horse with woman rider. The horse is hollow-moulded in buff earthenware, painted in red, with indications of harness in dark red. There are holes for the ears, rider and tail, and rectangular slots for the legs. The woman is modelled very flat, with traces of paint on her face and dress.

> Ht. (with rider) $11\frac{3}{4}''$ L. $17\frac{1}{8}''$
> II–IV century
> *Cf.* Hoyt, *Cat.* 51

S. 30   Pl. 1b
Lion, sitting on his haunches with head lifted and left hind leg raised to scratch his head.

18

Vigorously modelled in dark grey pottery with traces of white and red pigment. Hollow, with hole in base.

Ht. $7\frac{1}{4}''$ Depth of stand $6\frac{1}{8}''$
Six Dynasties
Exhib.: BH 1935, 2415 ('Wei'); Dartington Hall 1949, 57; OCS 1953 (Pre-T'ang), 53 ('Wei')

S. 28   Pl. 2a

Standing figure of a pole- or standard-bearer in a long robe with full sleeves, and thick boots. Heavily modelled in dark grey clay covered with a white slip showing traces of red and black paint.

Ht. $21\frac{5}{8}''$
III or IV century
Cf. Eumo., *Cat.* VI, Pl. VII, f 26, f 29

S. 15   Pl. 2b

Standing attendant with head-dress, short jacket with long sleeves, and long trousers. He stands in an attitude of expectant servility, his hands clasped before him. The back is flat, the details of dress and hands sharply incised in dark grey clay. Faint traces of white slip under reddish-brown earth incrustation.

Ht. $21\frac{5}{8}''$
V–VI century
Publ. Eumo., *Cat.* VI, Pl. VII, f 27

S. 21   Pl. 3a

Dog with puppy. The dog is sitting; the puppy jumps up between her front paws to lick her head. Moulded dark grey clay finished with a knife; traces of red and black paint over a white slip.

Ht. $3\frac{1}{2}''$ L. $5\frac{7}{8}''$
Six Dynasties

S. 22   Pl. 3b

Head of a horse, modelled in dark grey clay with holes for the ears. Painted with red pigment over a thick white slip which gives a smooth surface. Indications of harness painted in white.

Ht. $5\frac{5}{8}''$ L. $6\frac{3}{4}''$
II–IV century
Cf. Eumo., *Cat.* I, Pl. XXI, 126

S. 10   Pl. 3c

Packhorse, with heavy grain-sacks slung over its saddle. Hollow-cast, delicately modelled dark grey clay, covered with white slip. Tail and legs broken and repaired.

Ht. $7\frac{3}{8}''$ L. $8\frac{3}{4}''$

VI or early VII century
Exhib.: BH 1935, 2416 ('Wei'); OCS 1947 (Figures), 24 ('Probably T'ang')
Cf. Hoyt, *Cat*. 77 ('Six Dynasties')

S. 35   Pl. 4a

Bactrian camel sitting on the ground. Mounted on his back, with one hand on the forward hump, is a bearded socratic Westerner, clad in a sheepskin coat with lapels, and high boots. From either side hang frames (of wicker or bamboo) on which are hung a waterflask, a sack, and a dead animal: these two sections are identical and were separately moulded and luted on. Hollow-cast, dark grey pottery, with traces of red and black paint over a white slip.

Ht. $6\frac{7}{8}''$ L. $8\frac{3}{4}''$
North China
Late VI or VII century
Illus. Mario Prodan, *The Art of the T'ang Potter* (London, 1960), Pl. 20
Cf. BH 1935, 2409; OCS 1953 (Pre-T'ang), 104

S. 13   Pl. 4b

Crouching dog. Dark grey pottery, the body painted red over a white slip; the tail, ears and muzzle are left black, while the sides of the face and eyes are white, picked out in black pigment.

Ht. $4''$ L. $7\frac{1}{4}''$
VI or VII century
Exhib.: BH 1935, 2425; Manchester 1936, 34; OCS 1947 (Figures), 24 ('T'ang');
   Dartington Hall 1949, 59; OCS 1955 (T'ang), 65 ('T'ang or earlier')
Publ. BH *Commem. Cat*. Pl. 107
Cf. Similar but slightly larger dog in coll. of H.M. the King of Sweden, *Cat*. Pl. 110, 2

S. 27   Pl. 5a

Bactrian camel, striding forward, its head raised and turned to the left. Perched astride on the saddle-bags between its humps is a young Chinese girl, in Central Asian (?) dress, who has twisted round to the left and is pointing with her left forefinger. Vigorously moulded buff pottery covered with golden-brown finely-crackled glaze, under which the trappings are modelled in flat relief. The shaggy hair on the camel's throat, dewlap, hocks and humps is unglazed and has a roughened texture. The girl's head and hands and part of the saddle-bags are also unglazed, and painted white over red; her hair is painted black. The elliptical stand is unglazed and painted red.

Ht. $15\frac{1}{2}''$ L. $11''$
T'ang Dynasty, VII century
Exhib.: Manchester 1936; OCS 1947 (T'ang), 28 ('Sui or T'ang'); OCS 1955
   (T'ang), 61

S. 4   Pl. 5b

Sleeping youth, seated on the ground with his head buried in his left arm. The dress, high boots (or puttees) and thick curly hair indicate a Western barbarian, probably a slave or camel boy. Dark grey pottery, with traces of red and white pigment.

Ht. $3\frac{5}{8}''$

VI or VII century

Exhib.: BH 1935, 2430; Manchester 1936, 6460; OCS 1947 (Figures), 25; OCS 1953 (Pre-T'ang), 7

Cf. Rather similar crouching and sleeping figure in H.M. the King of Sweden coll., *Cat.* Pl. 66, 4 ('Weeping figure'). Karlbeck reported that it came from Shansi

S. 32   Pl. 5c

Greyhound, in light buff pottery, moulded in two halves along its length, and partly covered with a thin golden-brown finely-crackled glaze.

Ht. $3\frac{1}{4}''$ L. $4''$

T'ang Dynasty

S. 3   Colour Pl. A

Pair of woman attendants, the one holding in her hands a lidded jar which is a miniature replica of Pl. 26a in the collection; the other holding a saucer from which the bowl (?) has been broken off. Their long-sleeved dresses are tied with bands around the breast which fall in straight lines down the front. Their hair is folded up into an elaborate coiffure. Pale buff pottery covered with a white slip; indications of red and green pigment on the dress. The upper part seems to be covered with a very thin transparent glaze.

Ht. $10\frac{1}{2}''$ and $10\frac{1}{4}''$ (with cup)

T'ang Dynasty, VII century

Cf. Hoyt, *Cat.* 123, two similar girls with stick (clapper?) and cymbals, and similar hair style; OCS 1955 (T'ang), 44; and similar but sturdier woman with larger jar, in the coll. of H.M. the King of Sweden; a figurine of a girl holding a jar of this type was among the *ming-ch'i* excavated from the Sui Dynasty tomb at Anyang referred to under Pl. 6b, below

S. 18   Pl. 6a

Set of four woman attendants. One holds a roll of cloth, one a goose, one a small child in a rattan basket holding a toy (?) animal; the fourth one has her hands clasped in her long sleeves. They wear a high-waisted gown fastened with a girdle tied and hanging down in front, a stole, lotus shoes and folded head-dress.

The body, hollow-cast in two halves (back and front), is of buff pottery, burnt red where exposed inside. The garments are painted in red and black over a white slip and show evidence of retouching. There are traces of greenish glaze under the black and other patches of glaze, perhaps accidental, elsewhere. The head and neck are covered with a thick white slip on which the features are picked out in black, with traces of pink flesh-tints on the face.

Ht. $14\frac{3}{8}''$ and $14\frac{1}{2}''$ (the one holding a child)
T'ang Dynasty (before 750)
Exhib.: OCS 1947 (Figures), 26; OCS 1955 (T'ang), 24

S. 1 Pl. 6b

Girl sitting on the ground, holding a winnowing-basket against her lap with her left hand while in her right she holds three small egg-shaped objects; four more lie in the basket. Buff pottery. The girl's face has a pinkish tint, the features being picked out in black and red, the hair, piled and folded on top of her head, being also painted black; the exposed part round her shoulders is covered with a thin finely-crackled ivory glaze; and her clothing and basket are painted red and blue.

The face has been restored, the glaze having been replaced by a pinkish varnish; the neck has been repaired and touched up. The red pigment covering her dress has been applied over a thin, crackled ivory glaze; elsewhere (e.g. on knees and basket), there is no glaze underneath, but the colour has probably been strengthened.

Ht. $6\frac{1}{4}''$
VII century
Exhib.: BH 1935, 2410 ('Wei or T'ang'); Manchester 1936, 31; OCS 1947 (Figures), 27; Dartington Hall 1949, 62
Cf. Hoyt, *Cat.* 69 (girl is one of set of four peasant figures). A similar but uncoloured girl holding a winnowing basket was among the ninety-one objects, chiefly ceramic figurines, unearthed from the tomb of a certain Chang Sheng, who was buried at Anyang in A.D. 595. See *Kaogu*, 1959.10, pp. 541–45

S. 16 Pl. 7a

Horse, with right foreleg raised and head turned back biting his left shoulder. Hollow-cast in light buff pottery, the heavy dressed mane being made separately and luted on. The body is coloured red, the head and saddle painted in white slip, the eyes and bridle picked out in black. The mane is painted dull chocolate red. The mane and neck appear to be restored, and there is some retouching on the head.

Ht. $16\frac{1}{2}''$ L. $2' 3''$
T'ang Dynasty
Exhib.: OCS 1947 (Figures), 11; OCS 1955 (T'ang), 50
Illus. full page in *Trans. OCS* 1954–55, Pl. 31

S. 14 Pl. 7b

Pair of dancing girls, each with one arm raised, and long trailing sleeves. They wear a short high-waisted jacket and belt, a long skirt and high pointed coiffure. Hollow-cast dark grey pottery, face and chest covered with white slip, features picked out in black. The jacket has a red border and red lining, the border originally gilded.

Ht. $11\frac{3}{4}''$ and $11\frac{5}{8}''$
Probably VI or early VII century
Exhib.: OCS 1947 (Figures), 3 ('Six Dynasties'); Dartington Hall 1949, 60; OCS 1955 (T'ang), 27 ('T'ang or Earlier')

S. 33   Pl. 8a

Standing woman with long trailing sleeves and splayed skirt forming a wide base. The short jacket and long skirt are vigorously modelled on the back, the skirt being pleated. The two holes left for separate hands (now missing) suggest that she held something before her which would have concealed her middle, thus making it unnecessary to model the dress with the care shown on the back. Her hair is drawn back, looped up in a chignon.

Dark grey clay, covered with white slip; the neck and sleeves of the robe are ornamented with a broad band in brick red and a narrow edge of dark red. The features are picked out in black; the hair is black. A gold head-band (a later restoration) lies across hair above forehead.

Ht. $23\frac{1}{2}''$

VI or VII century

S. 9   Pl. 8b

Animal, probably a *ch'i-lin*, sitting on his haunches, with short bushy tail, three spines on his back and vestigial wings on his shoulders. His teeth are bared in a ferocious snarl. Hollow-moulded buff pottery, burnt reddish where exposed. Covered with a thin olive-brown finely-crackled glaze. The spines, wings, part of the head, and the front from throat to base between the forelegs are unglazed and covered with white slip, which across the chest is painted in horizontal parallel lines.

Ht. $14\frac{5}{8}''$

Place of origin uncertain, but probably Chekiang; Szechwan (Chengtu) is also a possibility

VI or early VII century

Cf. Hoyt, *Cat.* 127, a pair of *ch'i-lin* with very similar modelling, in pinkish clay, greenish-white glaze and traces of black and red paint. Dated T'ang Dynasty

S. 25   Pl. 9a

Tired horse. Hollow-moulded in white pottery, the details finished with a knife, and covered with a white slip. The eyes are outlined in black; the mouth, nostrils and mane picked out in red. The modelling is unusually sensitive.

The legs and tail have been repaired.

Ht. $7\frac{5}{8}''$ L. $10\frac{1}{4}''$

North China

T'ang Dynasty

Exhib.: OCS 1947 (Figures), 41; Dartington Hall 1949, 63

S. 6   Pl. 9b

Bird with human head and beak, the head bent back and turned to the right. Dark grey clay, covered with pink slip; the wings and tail painted black and white, with red in the grooves; the top-knot and eyes picked out in black. Minute traces of gilding on head and neck. There is a hole under the tail.

Ht. $3\frac{3}{8}''$ L. $6\frac{5}{8}''$

T'ang Dynasty

FIGURINES

S. 17c & d   Pls. 10a & b

Pair of camel-drivers, dressed in belted tunic open at the neck, and high boots; the right hand is raised, and both fists clenched.

The body is hollow-cast in two sections in light buff pottery, and covered with a golden-brown and green finely-crackled glaze. The unglazed base, hands and head are covered with a white slip.

Ht. $17\frac{5}{8}''$ and $17\frac{3}{8}''$
North China
T'ang Dynasty
Exhib.: OCS 1947 (Figures), 131, one, with one of the camels (Pl. 17a)

S. 17a   Pl. 10a

Bactrian camel, one of a pair, with head raised and turned a little to the right. It has a flounced saddle-cloth to which are attached frames on either side; the right frame carries a sack, flanked by a pitcher with fluted neck and a round object which may be a skin of butter; the left frame carries, to one side of the sack, a flask with moulded decoration on the body and loop-handles on the shoulder, to the other a haunch of meat. Across the back between the humps lies a heavy saddle worked at each end in the form of a monster mask.

Hollow-cast buff pottery, covered with green, golden-brown and cream glaze. The flat base is unglazed. Much broken and repaired. Cast from the same mould as Pl. 10b.

Ht. $27\frac{1}{4}''$ L. $19''$
North China
T'ang Dynasty
Exhib.: OCS 1947 (Figures), 131 (with one driver)
Cf. Eumo., *Cat.* I, Pl. XL, 278

S. 17b   Pl. 10b

Bactrian camel, with head raised and turned a little to the right. His back is covered with a flounced saddle-cloth decorated with a diaper pattern, with holes for the humps.

Hollow-cast buff pottery, covered with a cream glaze splashed with green and golden-brown.

On the upper side of the base is incised an inscription in some non-Chinese script. Legs, neck and mouth repaired. Cast from the same mould as Pl. 10a.

Ht. $27\frac{1}{4}''$ L. $19''$
North China
T'ang Dynasty

S. 7   Pl. 11a

Saddled horse, standing with his head turned a little to the left. Hollow-cast light buff pottery, covered, except for the saddle, with a golden-brown glaze paling to cream on the nose and mane; eight of the nine tassels hanging from the surcingle are glazed green.

Ht. $19\frac{5}{8}''$ L. $19\frac{3}{8}''$ plus tail
North China

FIGURINES

T'ang Dynasty
Said to have been formerly in the collection of Li Hung-chang

S. 24   Pl. 11b

Woman feeding a small parrot, which she holds in her left hand, with a corncob in her right. Stoutly moulded, hollow-cast light buff pottery; patterns of rosettes on her girdle and cloud-scrolls on her under-robe are incised in the paste. The dress and shoes are covered with a cream, blue, green and golden-brown glaze; the corncob in golden-brown and cream glaze; the parrot green with brown on the head. Her head, hands and chest are unglazed and covered with a white slip, the eyes, eyebrows and hair picked out in black.

Ht. $16\frac{1}{8}''$
North China
T'ang Dynasty, first half of VIII century
Exhib.: OCS 1955 (T'ang), 22

S. 34   Pl. 12a

Pair of boys with upraised arms, the right fist clenched; they have thick curly hair and are clad in a *dhoti*. Probably dancers from Indo-China.[1] The two figures were cast from the same mould in pale buff earthenware, and covered with a greenish-yellow finely-crackled glaze. One figure is on a square base, and shows some decomposition of the glaze; the other, on a round base, has been broken and repaired at ankles and shoulder.

Ht. $11\frac{3}{8}''$
North China
T'ang Dynasty, VII century
Cf. Los Angeles 1957 (T'ang), 168

S. 31   Pl. 12b

Kneeling woman with hands raised as if holding a musical instrument. Pale buff pottery; the head, hands and shoulders are unglazed, covered with creamy-white slip; the hair, eyebrows and lips coloured. Upper part of dress and sleeves covered with pale green glaze; lower part and stand (representing a mat?) in darker green.

Ht. $8\frac{3}{8}''$
T'ang Dynasty
Exhib.: OCS 1955 (T'ang), 28

---

[1] Recently Jean Boisselier has drawn attention to the close resemblance between the style of a similar figure in the Musée Cernuschi and that of atlantids and dancers represented in sculpture on seventh-century Cham monuments at Mison and Trakieu, near the frontier between North and South Vietnam. He notes that a Chinese mission to Champa in 605 brought back to the capital Cham dancers, singers and musicians. He adds, 'C'est vraisemblablement un danseur originaire de ces régions que représente la statuette du Musée Cernuschi.' See 'Notes sur une statuette funéraire T'ang', *Arts Asiatiques* XXIV. 1 (1961), pp. 5–10. See also Jane Gaston Mahler, *The Westerners among the Figurines of the T'ang Dynasty of China*, Rome (1959), pp. 84–87, and Pls. XXIV and XXV, reproducing a number of similar figurines in Toronto, Chicago and Kansas City.

S. 19 Pl. 12c

Girl attendant in elaborate costume. Her hair is swept off her forehead and she wears a butterfly head-dress pierced in three places, presumably for feathers. The head is light grey clay burning darker grey where exposed, and covered with a white slip, the features delicately modelled. The eyebrows have been rather crudely retouched. The rest of the figure, made of a sugary white paste, burning light yellowish-buff, may be modern.

Ht. $12\frac{1}{2}''$

T'ang Dynasty (head only?)

Publ.: OA (N.S.) I, 2, Summer 1955, p. 57

S. 12 Pl. 13a

Man with strongly modelled semitic features; probably an Armenian (merchant?) with tall hat, loose, open short tunic, trousers, and right hand clenched over stomach. Light buff pottery with traces of red pigment on tunic, green on hat and undershirt, and black in eyes and hair.

Ht. $9\frac{3}{4}''$

T'ang Dynasty

Cf. Venice 1954, 311

S. 8 Pl. 13b

Dancing girl, moving to the right, her head thrown back, her arms raised. She wears a long skirt with flounced hem, three-quarter length jacket open at the neck and fastened with a girdle round her waist, with half-length sleeves plaited at the cuff and having long sweeping maniples. Her high coiffure is curled back in two loops on to her head. She wears high pointed shoes.

Modelled in dark grey clay covered with a thick white slip. The jacket is painted red with a gold border; the girdle is also gilded. The skirt is malachite green.

Ht. $9\frac{3}{4}''$

T'ang Dynasty

Exhib.: BH 1935, 2411

S. 11 Pl. 13c

Pair of seated women; one plays with a small dog who jumps up between her knees under her outstretched hands; the other, looking to the right, held some object (perhaps a musical instrument?) in her left hand, the first and second fingers of her right hand being extended. They wear the pointed 'Phrygian' cap and low-cut high-waisted dress fastened with a girdle. Dark grey pottery, hand modelled, with traces of white slip on head, breast and hands, red and green on the dress. The authenticity of these figures has been questioned.

Ht. $9\frac{1}{4}''$ and $9\frac{5}{8}''$ (with dog)

Early T'ang type

S. 36 Pl. 14

Lion, sitting on its haunches, its head turned to the right. The mane is close-set and composed of formalized curls; the bushy tail sweeps round over the right hind paw.

White marble. Stained brown; left side heavily encrusted as a result of burial.
Probably a tomb guardian figure.

Ht. $8\frac{1}{8}''$ Pedestal $4\frac{3}{4}'' \times 4\frac{1}{2}'' \times 1\frac{1}{4}''$

North China

VI or early VII century

Exhib.: OCS 1955 (T'ang), 329

Cf. Lion in Musée Guimet, Ht. 15 cm. (6"); BH 1935, 632; Marble lion in Nelson
Gallery, Kansas City, *publ.* Sickman and Soper, *The Art and Architecture of China*,
Pl. 61(B)

S. 5   Pl. 15

Figure of the goddess Kuanyin (the 'Goddess of Mercy'), seated on the ground with her
left knee raised in an attitude reminiscent of the Buddhist posture of 'royal ease'. White
porcelain, covered with a white glaze. Her head is turned to the right and she looks down
pensively. Her left hand rests on her knee, her right holds a small scroll. She wears a dia-
dem with the image of Shakyamuni in the centre; her piled-up head-dress is covered with a
scarf. The robes flow down over her body in rippling folds.

Ht. $8\frac{7}{8}''$ Greatest width $6\frac{1}{4}''$

Te-hua ware

XVII or early XVIII century

Exhib.: OCS 1947 (Figures), 77 ('XVIII century'); Dartington Hall 1949, 130; OCS
1957 (Ming), 96 ('XVII century')

Publ. Trans. OCS XXX, 1955–56, 1956–57, Pl. 30,96; Sullivan, *An Introduction to
Chinese Art*, Pl. 128

Cf. Honey, *Ceramic Art of China*, Pl. 144 (V. & A.) ('XVII–XVIII century')

2. Pre-T'ang Wares, other than Yüeh

C. 348   Pl. 16a

Jar with ovoid body, short neck and flaring mouth; with two loop-handles with attached moulded rings, and three raised bands round the shoulder. There is a combed wave-pattern incised in the clay above and below a plain band round the neck. Short roughly finished foot. Heavily-potted porcelanous stoneware, burnt reddish-brown. The upper half of the body and the inside of the lip are covered with a crackled olive green felspathic glaze, unevenly applied.

> Ht. $13\frac{5}{8}''$ Diam. $10\frac{1}{2}''$
>
> About III century
>
> *Cf.* Seligman coll., OCS 1953 (Pre-T'ang), 52; Fritz Low-beer coll., Los Angeles 1952, 30

C. 271   Pl. 16b

Vessel in the shape of a bird, with long straight tail forming the handle. Dark grey burnished clay.

> Ht. $5''$ L. $7\frac{7}{8}''$
>
> North China. Said to be from Hsün-hsien, Honan
>
> Warring States, IV–III century B.C.
>
> *Cf.* Hoyt, *Cat.* 12 (one of a pair), said to be from Loyang; rather large and elaborate specimen, with wings in slots, shown by Eumorfopoulos at OCS specimen meeting, *publ. Trans. OCS* 1928–30, Pl. II; Nelson Gallery, Kansas City; this and the Hoyt bird are discussed by Höchstädter, 'Pottery and Stoneware of Shang, Chou and Han', *BMFEA* 24 (1952), p. 92 and figs. 77 and 78. He states that this and vessels of the same ware are believed to come from Chin-ts'un (Loyang)

C. 351   Pl. 16c

Basin (*p'an*) with flat flanged rim, slightly recessed bottom, and flat base. Buff earthenware covered except for the base with a thin crackled green lead glaze, showing considerable decomposition and some iridescence.

Inside are seven small oval thinly-potted eared wine-cups (*yü-shang*) with thick flange decorated with a zigzag pattern. These show traces of green glaze, much decomposed.

The 'winged cups' imitate a common Han form in lacquer and metal. They also have been found in sets standing on a low tray.

> Basin: Ht. $2\frac{1}{2}''$ Diam. $12\frac{1}{2}''$
>
> Cups: Ht. $1\frac{1}{8}''-1\frac{3}{8}''$ Diam. $3\frac{1}{4}''-3\frac{1}{2}''$
>
> North China
>
> Han Dynasty
>
> *Cf. Sekai Tōji Zenshu* VIII, Pl. 72 (upper)

3. T'ang Coloured and White Wares of North China

It was in the full light of T'ang confidence and vigour that the art of the Chinese potter was finally set free from its ancient bondage to the bronze tradition — a confidence which showed itself in buoyant, high-shouldered contours, in bold experiments with coloured glazes, and above all in the way in which foreign shapes and decorative conventions were borrowed wholesale by the potters of North China, and given an unmistakably Chinese stamp.

The rich colours of the finely-crackled polychrome wares were thinly applied over a white slip, which gives them a wonderfully luminous clarity. These vessels and trays show a fascinating mixture of Western elements. The amphora (Pl. 24a) is a Greek shape that lingered on in Sasanian metalwork; the phoenix-head ewer (Pl. 25a) with its moulded decoration is likewise Near-Eastern, while some of the stamped motifs, such as the lotus and *hamsa* (goose) on the flat trays (Pl. 20a & b), derive from the iconography of Indian Buddhism. The peculiar technique of marbling (Pl. 22b) was known in ancient Rome, but was probably discovered independently by the Chinese potter.

In spite of the extensive excavations of the last ten years, relatively few T'ang kilnsites have come to light in North China. Only one group of kilns producing polychrome glazed wares has so far been identified. First investigated in 1957, they lie in Kung-hsien, thirty miles east of Loyang. The source of Hsing-yao, famous in literature, remains to be discovered, and nearly all the recently excavated material comes from tombs, a gratifying number of which — beginning with the celebrated grave of Pu Jen (A.D. 603) discovered by Dr. Li Chi while excavating at Anyang — are precisely dated or dateable. A survey of their contents suggests that the polychrome wares declined after the middle of the eighth century, perhaps because fewer people could afford them, although they continued in prosperous Szechwan well into the Sung Dynasty, while the tradition was handed on in the far Northwest under the Liao Dynasty (Pl. 23b) until its destruction in 1125.

Meanwhile new shapes of exquisite refinement, some of which were borrowed from metalwork, were being evolved in white porcelain, of which three distinct kinds can be identified in this collection. One has a thick, smooth, creamy-white uncrackled glaze of the type of the beautiful little jar (Pl. 27a); the second has a thinner glaze the colour of ivory, covered with a close, fine crackle, seen in the covered jar (Pl. 26a) and the bottle (Pl. 27b). The third type, an early form of *ch'ing-pai*, is represented by the exquisite wine-cup (Pl. 26c), and the tray on high foot (Pl. 27c). The latter is very similar to pieces in the Pu Jen tomb, and, like the wine-cup, could be as early as the seventh century.

It would be dangerous to be dogmatic about the date or place of origin of these wares. We may assume that there were kilns producing them within convenient reach of Loyang and Changan, while it seems probable that an early form of *ch'ing-pai* was already being produced in the region of Ching-te-chen. Some are certainly to be dated to the first decades of the T'ang Dynasty, while the two streams — ivory-white leading through Hsing-yao to Ting in the north, bluish-white leading to fine *ch'ing-pai* in Kiangsi — continued without

29

interruption into the Sung Dynasty. In addition, white wares were produced in Szechwan, Hunan and Chekiang, and possibly also in Kiangsu.

A tomb with a date equivalent to 933, discovered in 1956 outside the east gate of Hai-chow near the sea-coast of north Kiangsu, contained circular boxes of fine porcelain covered with a creamy-white glaze, bowls with foliate rim of a type generally considered as typically T'ang, and two pillows with peonies incised through the glaze. These pieces, coming midway between the end of T'ang and the beginning of Sung, form an important link between the two great epochs, and add proof, if proof were needed, that the period of political chaos dignified with the name of the Five Dynasties was an era of high achievement in ceramics, as it was in painting.

C. 253   Colour Pl. B

Globular jar with wide mouth, everted lip, and flat base. Pottery, covered with a white slip. Covered outside with a streaky deep blue glaze, stopping well short of the base. The lower half of the interior is covered with a thin yellow glaze. Three spur-marks on the rim.

Ht. $5\frac{5}{8}''$ Diam. $6\frac{1}{2}''$

Exhib.: OCS 1949 (T'ang), 37; OCS 1955 (T'ang), 92; Arts Council 1953, 4

Publ. Eumo., *Cat.* I, Pl. 51,336

Cf. Jar in Schiller coll. in City Art Gallery, Bristol, Venice 1954, 332; Mrs. Alfred Clark, Los Angeles 1952, 179; jar with cover, Russel Tyson coll., Los Angeles 1952, 61

C. 3   Pl. 17a

Ovoid jar with short neck, wide mouth and slightly everted lip, slightly splayed and concave base. Pinkish-white pottery covered outside with a thin finely-crackled rich amber glaze over a white slip, stopping in an uneven line around the lower part of the body. Three spur-marks on the inside of the lip.

Ht. $8\frac{1}{4}''$ Diam. $8\frac{1}{2}''$

Exhib.: OCS 1949 (T'ang), 172; Arts Council 1953, 1; OCS 1955 (T'ang), 94; Los Angeles 1956 (T'ang), 12

Illus. Honey, *Ceramic Art of China*, Colour Pl. A

Cf. Jar in the coll. of H. E. Giovanni Gronchi, Rome, Prodan, *The Art of the T'ang Potter*, Colour Pl. XVI

C. 4   Pl. 17b

Ovoid jar with short neck, wide mouth and slightly everted lip, on slightly splayed and bevelled flat base. Applied to the shoulder are four lion masks in low relief. Pinkish-white pottery, covered with thin mottled green, amber and white glaze over a white slip. Three spur-marks on the lip.

Ht. $6\frac{7}{8}''$ Diam. $8''$

C. 231   Pl. 18a

Vase with eight-lobed ovoid body, long neck and flaring foliated lip; with horizontal incisions on neck and above base. Light buff earthenware covered with a finely-crackled iridescent and partly encrusted green glaze over a white slip. The base is recessed, forming

B. Jar. Pottery, covered with blue glaze over a white slip. Ht. $5\frac{5}{8}''$. T'ang Dynasty. (C.253, page 30)

a foot, and partly filled with plaster. Possibly this was done at a later date to make it look like a T'ang base. The glaze has the typical T'ang fine crackle.

Said to be from Ch'ing-ho-hsien (between Chü-lu-hsien and Tz'u-chou).

Ht. 9″ Diam. 5″

IX–X century

Exhib.: OCS 1949 (T'ang), 135; Dartington Hall 1949, 70; Arts Council 1953, 3; OCS 1955 (T'ang), 138; OCS 1960 (Sung), 116

Cf. Two similar vases in the collection of Mrs. Alfred Clark, one covered with green glaze, the other with white, both having a splayed and grooved foot; vase in the collection of Mrs. Walter Sedgwick, cream glaze, *publ.* OCS 1960 (Sung), 115

C. 27 Pl. 18b

Small ovoid jar with everted lip and flat base. Light buff pottery with a cream slip. A thin, rich, minutely-crackled green glaze, partly iridescent and stained by burial, runs unevenly down the side, in one place reaching the base. Unglazed inside.

Ht. 3″ Diam. $3\frac{1}{2}$″

Exhib.: Venice 1954, 333

C. 7a Pl. 18c

Bowl of white pottery, decorated outside with a moulded pattern of dotted scales, the base ornamented with moulded formalized flowerlets within a circle. Three spur-marks inside bottom. Covered inside and out with a finely-crackled mottled cream, green and golden-brown glaze.

Ht. $1\frac{1}{2}$″ Diam. $3\frac{7}{8}$″

C. 7b Pl. 18d

Bowl of white pottery, with three spur-marks on the base. Decorated outside with two bands of formalized flowerlets impressed round the rim, above a roughly symmetrical design of raised scrolls surrounded by flowerlets. Covered outside with a rich golden-brown finely-crackled glaze; the inside is covered with a cream, green and golden-brown glaze which is worn away in the raised centre of the cream areas. The bowl has been broken in half and repaired.

Ht. $1\frac{3}{8}$″ Diam. $3\frac{3}{4}$″

C. 105 Pl. 19a

Shallow dish, with low sloping side and everted lip, on a wide, shallow slightly splayed foot. Heavily-potted light buff stoneware, covered with a thick bluish-black glaze. Suffused with spots and splashes of phosphatic glaze ranging in colour from white through cream to turquoise blue. The glaze, which is brownish-black outside, runs down unevenly around the foot.

Ht. $1\frac{7}{8}$″ Diam. $9\frac{7}{8}$″

Exhib.: OCS 1949 (T'ang), 143; OCS 1952 (Chün and Brown), 135; Venice 1954, 378; OCS 1955 (T'ang), 231; Los Angeles 1957, 245

Cf. Dish in Eumo., *Cat.* I, Pl. LIII, 439

C. 377   Pl. 19b

Wine-cup with slightly everted lip and short, splayed and slightly concave base. Earthenware, covered with a thin minutely crackled cream glaze streaked golden-yellow and green, and running to thick dark green drops on the foot. A faint double incision runs around outside below the rim.

Ht. $2\frac{3}{4}''$ Diam. $3\frac{5}{8}''$

Cf. The same shape in T'ang glass, Kempe coll., OCS 1955 (T'ang), 302, 303

C. 363   Pl. 19c

Ovoid jar with short neck and everted lip, on a short slightly splayed and bevelled flat base. Two small loop-handles on the shoulder. Light buff stoneware partly burnt reddish-brown, and covered with a dark matt greenish-brown tea-dust glaze, splashed with thick greyish-cream, and stopping short of the base.

The decoration of this group of pieces shows an adventurous gaiety, particularly in the casual yet brilliant handling of the white splashes, that is unique in the history of ceramics.

Ht. $4\frac{7}{8}''$ Diam. $4\frac{1}{2}''$

Cf. Jar in BM, purchased in 1923; Rücker-Embden Pl. 11, in colour

C. 364   Colour Pl. C

Ewer with ovoid body, wide neck and flaring mouth, with short tapering spout on the shoulder and strap handle. Fine light buff stoneware, covered with a glaze ranging from olive-brown to black, with thick patches of streaky glaze ranging from cream through grey to turquoise blue. The glaze, which shows a fine crackle where it is thinnest, stops short of the flat bevelled base in a sweeping curve.

Ht. $5\frac{3}{4}''$ Diam. $4\frac{1}{2}''$

Cf. Riesco coll., OCS 1955 (T'ang), 228

C. 106   Pl. 20a

Flat offering dish with everted rim, standing on three short legs. Pottery, covered with a white slip and cream finely-crackled glaze. In the centre is a medallion containing a white and yellow goose flying amid white clouds on a green ground, surrounded by alternate lotus flowers and fungi; in deep blue, yellow and green glazes. The colours are outlined with grooves cut through the glaze into the body. The goose (*hamsa*) and lotus are both Buddhist symbols, the fungus an emblem of longevity or immortality. The shape of the tray, and the technique of decoration, derive from Sasanian metalwork.[1]

Ht. $2\frac{1}{2}''$ Diam. $11\frac{3}{8}''$

Exhib.: OCS 1949 (T'ang), 153; Venice 1954, 378

Cf. OCS 1957 (T'ang), 77; Hoyt, *Cat.* 92; *Sekai Tōji Zenshu* IX, Pl. 77

C. 110   Pl. 20b

Flat dish on three feet with everted rim. Pottery, covered with a finely-crackled cream glaze over a white slip. In the centre a formalized flower surrounded by a band of six

[1] See Willetts, *Chinese Art* II (London, 1958), pp. 494–500; and Gyllensvärd, *T'ang Gold and Silver*, fig. 22.

palmettes linked together, these designs being filled with green and dark blue glazes, the outlines cut through the glaze into the paste. A good example of a well-known type.

Ht. $1\frac{3}{4}''$ Diam. $7\frac{1}{2}''$
Exhib.: Arts Council 1953, 6

C. 344 Pl. 21a

Vase with high shoulder, tapering body, narrow neck and everted lip, standing on a slightly splayed and rounded foot. Lightly-potted buff earthenware, showing wheel-marks on the side; covered with a streaky finely-crackled greenish-brown glaze which stops just short of the base in an even line.

Ht. $8\frac{7}{8}''$ Diam. $4\frac{7}{8}''$
X–XI century

C. 378 Pl. 21b

Ovoid jar with wide mouth and slightly concave base. Heavily-potted buff stoneware covered with a thin crackled olive-brown glaze streaked with a suffusion ranging from yellowish-cream to rich turquoise blue, and stopping short of the base in a wavy line. The thick everted lip is a later restoration.

Ht. $10\frac{7}{8}''$ Diam. $9''$
Cf. Eumo., *Cat.* I, Pl. LIII, 439; similar but smaller jar in Ingram collection, MEA
      Oxford, Los Angeles 1957, 242

C. 6 Pl. 21c

Cup in the form of half a nautilus shell. Hard white pottery completely covered with a mottled, finely-crackled cream, green and golden-brown glaze.

Ht. $2\frac{1}{4}''$ Diam. $4''$
Exhib.: Arts Council 1953, 7
Cf. Eumo., *Cat.* I, Pl. LIX, 344, now in the BM; another in the coll. of E. H. North,
      Esq., London

C. 161 Pl. 21d

Begging bowl with flattened globular body imitating a metal shape. Extremely heavily potted earthenware covered with a white slip, and a finely-crackled green glaze running to thick black globules on the base. On the base also are three rough oblong spur-marks radiating from the centre.

Ht. $2\frac{7}{8}''$ Diam. $6''$
Exhib.: OCS 1949 (T'ang), 47; Arts Council 1953, 2; OCS 1955 (T'ang), 123
Publ. Eumo., *Cat.* I, 378
Cf. Pl. 30b in this coll.

C. 381 Pl. 22a

Globular wide-mouthed bowl with thickened rim and short tapering octagonal spout and splayed and bevelled foot, concave inside the base. Earthenware, covered with a pinkish slip, under a finely-crackled cream and deep blue glaze streaked with orange. The interior is glazed orange-brown. The spout is a later restoration.

Ht. $3\frac{1}{2}''$ Diam. $4\frac{3}{4}''$

Exhib.: Musée de l'Orangerie, Paris 1937

C. 309A   Pl. 22b

Flat dish with flanged lip, on three short feet. Three spur-marks on the upper surface. Marbled cream and chocolate-brown clay covered on the upper surface, underside of rim and round base of feet, with a thin finely-crackled cream glaze with a light golden-greenish tinge where it runs thick.

Ht. $1''$ Diam. $5\frac{1}{4}''$

Exhib.: OCS 1949 (T'ang), 142

Cf. Eumo., *Cat.* I, Pl. LXXV 520; Hoyt, *Cat.* 177

C. 382   Pl. 23a

Ewer with ovoid body and trumpet neck, strap handle, short straight spout and splayed flat base. Light buff earthenware covered with a thin uneven finely-crackled green glaze over a white slip, stopping well short of the base in an uneven line.

Ht. $8''$ Diam. $4\frac{1}{2}''$

Cf. Eumo., *Cat.* I, Pl. 68; Hobson, *Chinese Pottery and Porcelain*, Pl. 8, fig. 3; same shape in coloured glazes, *Sekai Tōji Zenshu* IX, p. 202, fig. 110

C. 286   Pl. 23b

Slender vase, with baluster-shaped body and trumpet neck, square-cut foot and recessed base. Horizontal grooving here and there on neck and body. Hard earthenware covered with a thin crackled turquoise green glaze, over a white slip, stopping in uneven tear-drops round the body.

Ht. $13\frac{1}{4}''$ Diam. $5\frac{1}{8}''$

Liao Dynasty

Exhib.: OCS 1949 (T'ang), 33 ('T'ang'); OCS 1955 (T'ang), 157 ('Liao')

Cf. Very similar vase in Mount Trust, OCS 1960 (Sung), 124; Hoyt, *Cat.* 171 ('Jehol type')

C. 265   Pl. 24a

Funeral amphora with ovoid body, slightly splayed and bevelled flat base, slender ridged neck and cup-shaped mouth with everted rim. Two strap-handles terminate in the heads of dragons who have seized the mouth-rim in their gaping jaws.

Whitish earthenware covered with a thin unevenly-crackled cream glaze with a greenish tint where it runs thick, and stopping high on the body in two sweeping curves.

Ht. $14\frac{3}{8}''$ Diam. $8\frac{1}{4}''$

VII–VIII century

Cf. Eumo., *Cat.* I, Pl. 48, A 323 and A 325; Hoyt, *Cat.* 129; V. & A., *publ.* Honey, *Ceramic Art of China*, Pl. 21, etc.

C. 345   Pl. 24b

Bowl with flattened globular ribbed body, wide mouth and slightly everted lip, standing on three legs in the form of tigers' feet. Light buff pottery covered with a white slip, burnt pinkish in firing. There are traces of a light greenish-brown crackled glaze here and there on body and feet.

Ht. $5\frac{1}{8}''$ Diam. $8\frac{1}{4}''$

VII–VIII century

C. 235   Pl. 25a

Ewer with flattened pear-shaped body and slender neck terminating in the head of a bird with a pearl in its beak, its flattened crest forming the mouth of the vessel. The handle sprouts in scrolls from the back of the bird's head and ends in scrolls on the body. The lower part of the body is splayed out to form a flat base. Light buff earthenware, made in two halves luted together vertically, covered with a finely-crackled partially iridescent and decomposed cream glaze with greenish tinge over a white slip.

One side of the body is decorated with a strutting phoenix in relief standing on a highly formalized floral spray and surrounded by other sprays; on the other side is a mounted hunter, turning in the saddle and drawing his bow in the manner of the Western barbarians. He, too, is surrounded by formalized floral sprays.

Ht. $12\frac{7}{8}''$ Diam. (of body) $5\frac{7}{8}''$

Cf. Hoyt, *Cat.* 132; similar vase with coloured glazes *publ.* Bluett, *Chinese Pottery and Porcelain in the Collection of Mr. and Mrs. Alfred Clark*, Pl. 11, fig. IV; Eumo., *Cat.* I, Pl. LXVI, 390; examples in metalwork *illus.* in Gyllensvärd, *T'ang Gold and Silver*, fig. 23; this shape and its Near Eastern prototypes are discussed in detail by Willetts in his *Chinese Art* II, pp. 477–79

C. 366   Pl. 25b

Ovoid jar with short neck and wide mouth, and splayed flat base; round the shoulder are four loop-handles and two light incised rings. Fine light grey stoneware, covered with a thin finely-crackled cream glaze with a faint bluish tint, over a white slip, showing slight decomposition and stopping unevenly short of the base.

Ht. $11\frac{1}{4}''$ Diam. $9\frac{1}{4}''$

VII or early VIII century

Cf. Very similar one in Lord Hollenden coll., OCS 1949 (T'ang), 61 ($10\frac{7}{8}''$); Hoyt, *Cat.* 135; Harkness coll. in Cleveland Museum of Art, Los Angeles 1952, 91

C. 390   Pl. 25c

Ovoid jar with thickened and everted lip, and four loop-handles high on the shoulder. Buff rather roughly-potted stoneware, covered with a finely-crackled brown glaze which stops well short of the concave base in an uneven line. Has been badly broken and repaired.

Ht. $5\frac{3}{4}''$ Diam. $5\frac{7}{8}''$

VI–VII century

T'ANG COLOURED AND WHITE WARES OF NORTH CHINA

C. 1   Pl. 26a

Jar with cover. Depressed globular body and flanged everted mouth; wide, slightly recessed foot. Cover has recessed knob. White porcellanous ware, covered with a finely-crackled cream glaze with a greenish tint where thick, and stopping short of the foot in an uneven line. Underside of cover unglazed.

The girl in Colour Pl. A in this collection is carrying a miniature vessel of this type.

Ht. $4\frac{3}{4}''$ Diam. $5\frac{1}{8}''$

Exhib.: OCS 1949 (T'ang), 95; Arts Council 1953, 10

Cf. Eumo., *Cat*, VI, f 60; Hoyt, *Cat.* 146; H.M. the King of Sweden coll., *Cat.*, girl holding one of these vessels, Pl. 72, full-size one, Pl. 115; Komor coll. Los Angeles 1957 (T'ang), 224; Japanese coll. in marbled ware, *Sekai Tōji Zenshu* IX, Pl. 96 (upper); smaller specimen in bronze (incorrectly labelled Han) in BM (formerly Eumorfopoulos coll.).

The earliest dateable example I have come across is in Yüeh celadon, excavated from a Chin Dynasty tomb dated 345 at Nanking, illustrated in *Kaogu* 1959 6, Pl. 5

C. 2   Pl. 26b

Wine-cup with slightly everted rim, on small, splayed and chamfered foot, slightly concave on the base. White porcellanous ware, covered with creamy-white widely-crackled glaze with greenish tint where it runs thick, and stopping short of the base in an uneven line.

Ht. $3\frac{1}{2}''$ Diam. $4\frac{7}{8}''$

VII century

Exhib.: Dartington Hall 1949, 69; Arts Council 1953, 8; OCS 1955 (T'ang), 161

Illus. in Honey, *The Art of the Potter* (London, 1946), Pl. 13A, p. 20: 'This shows a typical T'ang form and one of the most beautiful in all pottery. It is also an excellent illustration of the truth that pottery cannot be judged by the eye alone. Here the distribution of weight, a thinning of the edge towards the lip, the subtle thickening of wall towards the rounded base, and the solid foot, all help to give an indefinable feeling of "balance" in the hand; and these things count as much in the aesthetic impression given by the cup as the distinction of its profile, with its dynamic swelling and slight out-turning at the lip, which is all that can be shown in a photograph.'

Cf. Kempe coll. (Lindberg, 'Hsing-yao . . .' 33, Pl. 39); Hoyt, *Cat.* 147, pair of cups $3\frac{3}{4}''$ high; H.M. the King of Sweden coll., *Cat.* Pl. 70, $4\frac{1}{4}''$, white pottery; V. & A., *publ.* Honey, *The Ceramic Art of China*, Pl. 33a, white earthenware; Eumo., *Cat.* I, Pl. LII, 384, Ht. 3"; Koyama, *Chinese Ceramics, 100 Masterpieces*, Pl. 36, shows five of these cups and a circular pottery tray with three ring feet, Japanese coll.

C. 22   Pl. 26c

Stem-cup, with slightly everted lip on small stand. Translucent light buff porcellanous ware with pale blue glaze, imperfect on stem. Underside of flat base unglazed.

Ht. $3\frac{1}{8}''$ Diam. $3\frac{1}{4}''$

Ch'ing-pai type, North China

VIII century

Exhib.: OCS 1949 (T'ang), 63; Arts Council 1953, 54 ('Sung or earlier'); OCS 1955
     (T'ang), 189

Publ. Trans. OCS 1944–45, Pl. 23 ('T'ang')

Cf. Hoyt, *Cat.* 354 ('Ying-ch'ing type, T'ang Dynasty'); Seligman coll., OCS 1955
     (T'ang), 190, *publ.* Willetts, *Chinese Art* II, Pl. 38b; ROM, *publ.* Mario Prodan,
     The Art of the T'ang Potter (London, 1960), Pl. 21

C. 129   Pl. 27a

Ovoid jar, with everted lip and flat base, of greenish-white porcellanous ware, covered
with a creamy-white glaze. There is a fine crackle, more evident on lower part, around
shoulder and rim. Base unglazed.

Ht. $4\frac{3}{8}''$ Diam. $5''$

Exhib.: OCS 1949 (T'ang), 51

Cf. Jar in the coll. of Mrs. Alfred Clark

C. 148   Pl. 27b

Bottle of white porcellanous ware, with ovoid body, slender neck and everted rim, on a
thick, shallow chamfered foot. Covered with a crackled ivory glaze with a greenish tint
when it runs thick, and stopping short of the foot in an uneven line. This beautiful shape is
also found in T'ang silverware.

Ht. $10\frac{1}{4}''$ Diam. $4\frac{3}{4}''$

VIII–IX century

Exhib.: OCS 1949 (T'ang), 27; Dartington Hall 1949, 71; Arts Council 1953, 9

Cf. Former Alexander coll., Hobson, Rackham and King, *Chinese Ceramics in Private
     Collections*, p. 4, fig. 2; former Winkworth coll., Honey, *The Art of the Potter*, Pl.
     12; Gyllensvärd, *T'ang Gold and Silver*, fig. 35f, Pl. 23a

C. 274   Pl. 27c

Tray, with everted rim, standing on a high splayed foot. Whitish earthenware covered
with a fine greenish-white crackled glaze. Pedestal foot hollow and unglazed inside.

While many T'ang shapes owe their origin to Western metalwork, this can be traced
back to prehistoric China. A very similar tray in burnished black pottery was discovered in the
neolithic site of Liang-chu in Chekiang in 1955; another, in bronze, was excavated from the
tomb of the Marquis of Ts'ai in Shou-hsien, Anhui (*c.* 490–450 B.C.).[1]

Ht. $4\frac{5}{8}''$ Diam. $6\frac{1}{4}''$

North China white ware

VIII century

Exhib.: Venice 1954, 344; OCS 1955 (T'ang), 160

Cf. Lovely little tray with green glaze, BM, Oppenheim Bequest, 1947; Hoyt, *Cat.*
     141; H.M. the King of Sweden coll., *Cat.* Pl. 70,1; Eumo., *Cat.* I, Pl. XLVII, 321

[1] They are illustrated in William Watson, *Archaeology in China* (London, 1960),, Pls. 28 and 72.

C. 310   Pl. 27d

Box with cover. White porcellanous ware, very delicately potted. Cover moulded in the shape of three lotus leaves with beaded edges, and conventionalized bud in the centre. White glaze, greenish-brown where thick. Rims, part of interior, low foot and part of base unglazed. Rim chipped. The shape is closely copied from T'ang silverware.

Ht. $1\frac{5}{8}''$ L. $3\frac{1}{2}''$
North China white ware
VIII–X century
Cf. Gyllensvärd, *T'ang Gold and Silver*, Pl. 8c

C. 177   Pl. 28a

Shallow bowl in the form of an incense-burner on three animal feet. Pinkish pottery, covered with a finely-crackled cream glaze over a white slip. The glaze is much decomposed and stained, with some iridescence in the bottom.

The shape of the bowl, without the legs, is derived from T'ang metalwork.

Ht. $3''$ Diam. $6\frac{3}{4}''$
Exhib.: OCS 1949 (T'ang), 115; Venice 1954, 342
Cf. OCS 1955 (T'ang), 159; Venice 1954, 341; Gyllensvärd, *T'ang Gold and Silver*,
   fig. 1, a, b, c, e, f, Pls. 5a, 8a

C. 199   Pl. 28b

Bowl, the body of which is shaped in ten lobes, standing on a small foot. White translucent porcellanous ware, covered with an opaque creamy-white glaze. A spot of dark brown iron oxide inside near the rim. Glaze ends in an uneven line, partly covering the outside of the foot-rim on one side. The shape derives from Sasanian metalwork, and is found in Chinese beaten silver.

Ht. $1\frac{1}{2}''$ Diam. $4''$
VIII–X century
Exhib.: Arts Council 1953, 47
Cf. the same shape in beaten silver *illus.* in Gyllensvärd, *T'ang Gold and Silver*, figs.
   21c to 21g

C. 340   Pl. 28c

Shallow bowl with everted rim, standing on a low chamfered foot. Whitish porcellanous paste, finished on lower part of body and inside base with a knife. Covered with an ivory-white glaze with reddish discoloration, stopping well short of the base in an uneven line.

Ht. $1\frac{5}{8}''$ Diam. $4\frac{7}{8}''$
VIII–IX century
Cf. Bowls in Lindberg coll., *publ.* Lindberg, 'Hsing-yao . . .', Pls. 7, 8, 9

C. 112   Pl. 29a

Spittoon or slop-bowl with flattened globular body, widely flaring slightly inverted lip, small mouth and sharply-cut foot. Covered with a thick creamy-white glaze with faint

C. Ewer. Stoneware, covered with streaky phosphorous glaze. Ht. $5\frac{3}{4}''$. T'ang Dynasty. (C.364, page 32)

bluish-green tint where it runs thick on the outside, and stopping short of the base in an uneven line. Interior unglazed. A detail of the base is shown in Plate 144.

The shape is probably of Near Eastern origin.

Ht. $3\frac{3}{8}''$ Diam. $4\frac{3}{4}''$

VIII–X century

Exhib.: OCS 1949 (T'ang), 138

Cf. In Yüeh ware: Percival David Foundation No. 226, Los Angeles 1957 (T'ang), 249; Japanese coll., *Sekai Tōji Zenshu* IX, Pl. 43a; excavated from Yüeh kilns at Huang-shan-shan, on south-east of Shang-lin-hu, reported *K'ao-ku hsüeh-pao* 1959.3, p. 120 and Pl. IV

In white ware: Kempe coll., Venice 1954, 368; ROM, Toronto, Los Angeles 1957 (T'ang), 237

In Honan black ware: Ingram coll., MEA Oxford, Willetts, *Chinese Art*, Pl. 38A

In Hunan ware: BM, purchased 1952

In Liao green glazed ware: from Liao tomb in Inner Mongolia, *publ. Wen-wu* 1961.9

In inlaid Koryŏ celadon: in Duksoo Palace Museum, Kim and Gompertz, *The Ceramic Art of Korea*, Pl. 31

In glass: in Shōsōin Treasury, Nara, perhaps of Persian origin, *Cat.* III, Pl. 152

In silver: excavated from Yüan grave in Wu-hsien, Kiangsu, *publ. Wen-wu* 1959.11, 19–24; Kempe coll., Gyllensvärd, *T'ang Gold and Silver*, Pl. 20c

C. 325   Pl. 29b

Conical bowl on a sturdy square-cut foot with slightly recessed base. Light buff porcellanous ware, covered with a creamy glaze stopping short of the foot in an uneven line.

Ht. $1\frac{3}{4}''$ Diam. $4\frac{1}{4}''$

Possibly from kilns at P'ing-ting-yao, Shansi

IX–X century

Exhib.: OCS 1949 (T'ang), 71

C. 259   Pl. 29c

Circular box with cover on recessed shallow foot. White porcellanous stoneware. Lower half has delicately-finished inverted lip; lid has flattened knob. Cold creamy-white glaze with faint bluish tint applied to main part of the body and lid, inside lower part of lower half, on upper surface of inverted lip, and in centre of underside of lid. Shallow base unglazed. A detail of the base is shown in Plate 144.

Ht. $3\frac{1}{4}''$ Diam. $4\frac{1}{4}''$

IX–X century

Cf. Kempe coll., Venice 1954, 361; Lindberg coll., *publ.* Lindberg, 'Hsing-yao . . .', *BMFEA* 25, 1953, Pl. 17, No. 15 ('T'ang'); same shape, in coloured glazes, Hoyt, *Cat.* 120; *Sekai Tōji Zenshu* IX, Pl. 88 and fig. 169, etc.; for the same shape in copper, beaten silver and lacquer, Gyllensvärd, *T'ang Gold and Silver*, fig. 9, a to l

4. Hunan Wares

The simple, attractive wares produced in Hunan from the Han Dynasty to the Sung have become well known in the West, mainly through the enthusiastic collecting of Dr. Isaac Newton. For information as to their source, Western collectors have had to rely almost entirely upon the information supplied by Hongkong antique dealers, who had a simple rule-of-thumb method of identifying them. All were ascribed to Yo-chou or to Changsha, the T'ang-style pieces being generally attributed to Yo-chou, presumably because the *Ch'a-ching* said that Yo-chou kilns were active during the T'ang Dynasty, the earlier wares to Changsha, although there was then no evidence of the existence of any kilns in that city.

In spite of extensive excavations in and around Changsha, no pre-T'ang kilns have, at the time of writing, been discovered there. T'ang kilns have, however, now been definitely located in the city at Wang-ch'eng (*Wen-wu* 1959.5). The so-called Yo-yao is now known to have been made in kilns datable T'ang to Sung, in Hsiang-yin-hsien, on the right bank of the river at the point where the delta opens into the Tung-t'ing Lake. (See map.)

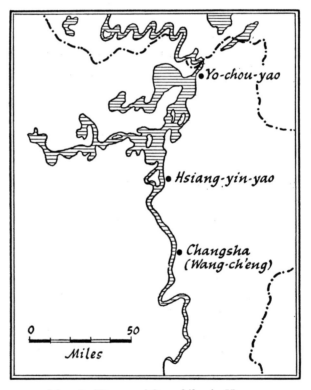

MAP I. T'ang and Sung kilns in Hunan

These kilns were investigated in 1953 and published later that year. Since then, kilns active during the Sung Dynasty have been discovered at Yo-yang (or Yo-chou) yet further to the north. At the time of writing, the report has not yet been published. From this it would seem, therefore, that the so-called Yo-chou wares of the T'ang Dynasty were actually

40

produced in Hsiang-yin-hsien, and not at Yo-chou. But nothing more definite should be said until the picture is clear.

The seven pieces in this collection all seem to be T'ang or pre-T'ang in date, and hence were probably made either in Changsha or in Hsiang-yin-hsien. They all have the characteristic Hunan celadon glaze — probably an attempt to imitate the more sophisticated Yüeh wares of Chekiang, which ranges in colour from reddish brown to a near-Yüeh olive, is but loosely married to the stoneware body and tends to flake off. To the pieces labelled by dealers as Yo-yao (presumably Hsiang-yin-hsien yao) the glaze was applied in two coats, the reddish body showing more clearly through the thin under-coat which often covers the whole vessel (Pl. 31b), while the thicker, crackled over-coat stops short of the base in an uneven line.

C. 111   Pl. 30a

Bowl on low slightly splayed and concave grooved foot. Hard buff stoneware. Decorated in the centre with a lotus pod surrounded by six petals, carved in the paste under a greyish-green crackled glaze, greener where it runs thick, and stopping unevenly short of the base.

Ht. $2\frac{1}{2}''$ Diam. $6''$

About VI century

Illus. by Gompertz, *Celadon*, Pl. 23A. He notes that 'similar examples are regarded in Japan as Hung-chou ware'.[1] However, he rightly says that this is doubtful, and recent Chinese explorations have failed to reveal any kilns at Hung-chou. A small bowl with a rosette stamped in the centre which, judging from a poor photograph in *K'ao-ku hsüeh-pao* 1959.3, Pl. 21 (after p. 105), appears to be of similar type, was found in a Sui Dynasty tomb at Changsha; another, in the possession of the Hongkong Government, is reproduced as a Six Dynasties piece by Mary Tregear, 'Changsha Pottery in Hongkong', *OA* (N.S.) VII, 3, Autumn 1961, p. 128

C. 341   Pl. 30b

Globular mendicant's bowl with large mouth, of thinly-potted grey stoneware covered inside and out with a thin, uneven, much crackled and partly decomposed olive-green glaze. Four spur-marks in bottom, five on the flat base.

Ht. $4\frac{1}{2}''$ Diam. $7\frac{1}{4}''$

V–VI century

Cf. An undecorated bowl of this shape, of white unglazed earthenware, Diam. $5\frac{1}{2}''$ is reproduced by Newton, *FECB* X, 3–4 (1958) as Pl. X, no. 39, labelled Han. But this shape is surely derived from an Indian Buddhist begging bowl. On the subject of Buddhist begging bowls (Ch. *po-to-lo*, Skt. *pātra*), see Willetts, *Chinese Art* II, 463–67. See also Pl. 21d in this coll.

[1] See *Sekai Tōji Zenshu* IX, Pl. 38 upper; bowl in Tokyo National Museum.

C. 333   Pl. 31a

Bowl on short, slightly splayed foot, five lobes indicated by ribs inside and incisions outside the body. Stoneware, covered all over with a thin olive-brown glaze showing some decomposition due to burial. Five spur-marks on the base.

Ht. $2\frac{1}{2}''$ Diam. $6''$

IX–X century

C. 349   Pl. 31b

Flat dish with slightly everted five-lobed rim, on thin foot. Hard-grained stoneware, covered with a finely-crackled olive-green glaze applied in two washes, the outer one stopping short of the base in an uneven line, the underglaze covering the base. Five spur-marks on the base

Ht. $1\frac{1}{2}''$ Diam. $7\frac{7}{8}''$

T'ang Dynasty

C. 372   Pl. 31c

Seven-lobed shallow bowl of buff stoneware covered with a yellowish-brown glaze over a slip. The glaze stops in an uneven line on the outside, is finely-crackled, and like the body is stained reddish by burial. The short foot is slightly concave. There are five spur-marks on the bottom.

Ht. $2''$ Diam. $6''$

T'ang Dynasty, VI–VII century

Cf. Rather similar bowls with foliate rim and spur-marks illustrated by Isaac Newton in *FECB* X, 3–4 (1958), Pl. XVI, No. 69c ('Six Dynasties'); Pl. XXIX, No. 138 ('T'ang'); Pl. XXXII, No. 154 ('T'ang')

C. 388   Pl. 32a

Incense-burner with cover, on a short bevelled foot, of hard fine-grained earthenware burnt red when exposed. The cover pierced with three holes above a flange of pinched-in paste, and surmounted by a small conical knob. A thin crackled glaze, shading from light brown to deep bluish-green where thick, is applied over a white slip to the side of the bowl, and to the upper part of the lid inside and out.

Ht. $3\frac{3}{4}''$ Diam. $3\frac{5}{8}''$

T'ang Dynasty

Cf. Isaac Newton, 'Chinese Ceramic Wares from Hunan', *FECB* X, 3–4 (1958), No. 147, Pl. XXXI, illustrates an incense-burner on four legs with bright green glaze. 'The glaze', he notes, 'is thinner on the green patches which suggests that the colour was produced by painting a chemical on the body before glazing and firing rather than by the addition of a splash of glaze over the basic glaze. . . . The glaze in the green areas is finely crazed and sometimes shows blue transmutation patches.'

C. 323   Pl. 32b

Wine-cup of fine-grained light buff earthenware on short slightly splayed and concave foot. Covered with a yellow crackled glaze which stops in an uneven line well short of the base. The glaze is much decomposed as a result of burial. Three spur-marks in the bottom.

Ht. $2\frac{3}{4}''$ Diam. $3\frac{5}{8}''$

T'ang Dynasty

Exhib.: Arts Council 1953, 14

C. 342   Pl. 32c

Shallow bowl with slightly everted rim and thick, short foot. Four lobes are indicated by nicks in the rim, ridges inside and corresponding crudely-cut grooves outside. Grey stoneware covered with a finely crackled greyish-green glaze stained red in the crackle by burial. The unglazed roughly cut foot and base are also stained red.

Ht. $1\frac{5}{8}''$ Diam. $5\frac{1}{8}''$

VI–VII century

C. 347   Pl. 32d

Ovoid jar of hard fine-grain earthenware with slightly everted lip and two small loop-handles. Covered with a heavily crackled greenish glaze with a tendency to flake. The glaze was evidently applied in two coats and stops unevenly short of the splayed flat base. Glazed inside.

Ht. $5\frac{1}{2}''$ Diam. $5\frac{1}{8}''$

T'ang Dynasty

5. Ju and Chün Wares

Of the thirty-one known pieces of Ju ware outside China, twenty-three are in England, fourteen being in the Percival David Foundation, and one in this collection. The beautiful dish (Pl. 33), is typical of this rarest of all Chinese wares. The buff, delicately-potted stoneware body is covered with an exquisite bluish-green glaze with a lavender-blue tint, netted over with a fine and delicate crackle — the first deliberate crackle in the history of Chinese ceramics.

It is only in the last thirty years that the identity of Ju ware has been finally settled. Japanese experts still hold firmly to the opinion that Ju and 'northern celadon' are two varieties of the same ware. This view, based on Harada's discovery of shards of both at kilnsites in Lin-ju-hsien, has not been accepted outside Japan, however; for while the two wares were evidently made in the same district, perhaps even in the same kilns, they are totally different in character. On the other hand, there seems to be an intimate relationship between Ju and the finest products of the Chün kilns at Shen-kou-chen in Yü-hsien which lay about fifteen miles east-south-east of Ju-chou.

It is well known that early in the twelfth century Ting ware was found unsatisfactory for court use, and that new kilns were set up at Ju-chou to make porcelain exclusively for the palace. At the same time, early sources state that during the Ta-kuan era (1107–11) or Cheng-ho era (1111–17) kilns were established at the capital to make *kuan* ware. This indicates that there were two official palace wares during the last decades of Northern Sung — Ju, and an as yet unidentified ware made at, or near, Kaifeng. Perhaps, as some writers have suggested, the latter was made by expert potters specially summoned to the capital from Ju-chou, or Chün-chou, or both. If so, then it might have combined the qualities of these wares, and a possible candidate might be the beautiful brush-washer in this collection (Pl. 34a), which Sir Percival David has called 'partly Chün and partly Ju, but best classified . . . as Northern Kuan'. Another name for pieces of this type is '*kuan* Chün'. But neither is entirely satisfactory. Strictly speaking, we are not entitled to call any ware *kuan*, whatever its quality, unless there is evidence that it was made for the palace, or unless we are prepared to accept without question the criteria of traditional Chinese connoisseurship. Ch'en Wan-li, in his brief history of celadon ware published in 1956, holds to the view that there were two *kuan* wares in this period, and that they were very closely related, though what the second one was he of course is unable to say. The similarity of the southern *kuan* ware, made in the Imperial Kilns at Hangchow, to Ju suggests that it was made to conform as closely as possible to it, and lends weight to the view that Ju was the *kuan* ware of the last years of Northern Sung.

It has been suggested that some borderline pieces between Ju, Chün and northern celadon might be examples of the Tung-yao which, according to the *Ko-ku yao-lun*, was similar, but inferior, to the imperial ware. Tradition holds that it was made in Ch'en-liu-hsien, just to the east of Kaifeng. But the district has been subject to repeated flooding; so far no kilns have ever been discovered there, and the identity of Tung ware has yet to be established.

44

JU AND CHÜN WARES

The whole question of the nature of 'northern *kuan*', and of its relationship with Ju, Chün and Tung, is wrapped in obscurity. The same ground has been gone over again and again, and much of what is said is sheer guesswork, based as it is on the chance survival of a very few early texts, the evidence of which is often conflicting, and on the jottings of two or three Ch'ing dilettanti. Now that the nature of the problem has been thoroughly stated by David, Gompertz, Garner and Ch'en Wan-li, it is unlikely that the written word will add anything but confusion to an already cloudy picture. The answer to these questions, if it is to be found at all, lies with the Chinese archaeologists who may one day lay bare the imperial kilns which must lie buried deep under, or near, the Northern Sung capital.

By contrast with the 'northern *kuan*', Chün ware presents relatively few problems. The main kilnsites at Shen-kou-chen in Yü-hsien are known to have been active from the Sung Dynasty to the present day, though it is unlikely that the lovely blue ware was made there after the Ming Dynasty.

A variety of Chün ware was also made at the Ju kilns in Lin-ju-hsien, another at Anyang, another in the recently discovered kilns at Hao-pi in T'ang-yin-hsien, and yet another at Ch'ing-wan-yao, about twenty miles west of Tz'u-chou. It was later copied with some success in Ming kilns in Szechwan, and at Te-hua in Fukien. Ching-te-chen made a porcelain version, of a brilliance lacking something of the soft warmth of the Sung original, while a rougher type was turned out by the Ming kilns at Fatshan and Shekwan, near Canton.

The most beautiful of all Chün wares are the bowls and dishes of sturdily potted greybuff stoneware, with brown slip on the unglazed base, covered with a thick iron glaze of an exquisite lavender-blue whose surface is pitted with burst bubbles. It was the Chün potters who discovered that spots of copper, oxidized in the glaze during firing, produced rich splashes of purple and crimson. The technique is probably derived from that of the black Honan stoneware with opalescent splashes, of which this collection contains several notable examples (Pl. 19a & c, Colour Pl. C). Used with restraint, these splashes lend an added depth and splendour to the blue glaze, but it seems that with the passage of time the colours became more extravagant, producing, especially in the much-prized bulb-bowls and flowerpots, most of which are probably Yüan or later, a lurid hue which Ming connoisseurs rudely dubbed 'mule's liver' or 'horse's lung'.

The brush-washer (Pl. 34a) is one of the very beautiful pieces of Chün ware which verge on Ju, and were probably of palace quality. They are hence sometimes called '*kuan* Chün'. Another attractive type is the so-called 'green Chün' (Pl. 37c), which reveals in its colour how closely related are Chün and northern celadon. The collection also contains a little specimen of the coarse-bodied 'soft Chün' (Pl. 39b), which some experts think may have been made in Canton as early as the Yüan Dynasty.

There would be good grounds for thinking that the legendary Ch'ai ware, made, according to the fourteenth-century *Ko-ku yao-lun*, on imperial order at Chengchow in the tenth century, might have been very close to Chün, at least in its glaze colour, although the same source says that its clay was a 'coarse yellow' where exposed at the foot. It is hard to believe that the colour of Ch'ai — about which later writers, who had never seen it, waxed so eloquent — could have been more beautiful than that of the finest Chün.

45

C. 218   Pl. 33

Brush-washer, with curved side, flat bottom, deep-set base and short foot splayed inside the rim. Entirely covered with a lavender-grey faintly-crackled glaze. Three spur-marks on the base. Repaired with gold at the lip.

Ht. $1\frac{1}{4}''$ Diam. $5\frac{1}{8}''$

Ju ware

North Sung Dynasty

Exhib.: OCS 1952 (Ju and Kuan), 1; Musée Cernuschi 1956, OCS 1960 (Sung), 64

Cf. Dish very similar but paler in colour and with larger crackle, in Percival David Foundation, A. 26

C. 92   Pl. 34a

Brush-washer in the form of a shallow bowl, with a horizontal projecting flange on one side, below the centre of which are the roots of a small loop-handle, now missing. There is no foot-rim, but the flat base has three spur-marks. Grey porcellanous body burnt reddish-buff where exposed. Covered with a soft lavender-blue finely-crackled and mildly opalescent glaze.

Ht. $2\frac{3}{4}''$ Diam. incl. flange $8''$

Chün ware

Sung Dynasty

Exhib.: OCS 1952 (Chün and Brown), 16 (Sir Percival David: 'an outstanding specimen of this type of ware, partly Chün and partly Ju in character, but best classified, I think, as Northern Kuan'); OCS 1960 (Sung), 42 ('Chün', 'this piece has affinities to Ju ware')

Cf. Brush-washer in Chün ware, Mrs. Blanco White coll. OCS 1952, 79; also Eumo., *Cat.* II, Pl. XXIV, B. 75; in soft Chün, Ingram coll., MEA Oxford, *Ibid.*, 196; in Kwangtung ware, Percival David Foundation No. A. 1; in Ting ware, Cheng Te-k'un coll., David, 'Céramiques Song', fig. 6

C. 321   Pl. 34b

Cup-stand with six-lobed foliate rim in the form of overlapping petals on splayed foot with chamfered foot-rim. Stoneware burnt reddish brown with traces of brown glaze where exposed on foot and rim; the rest covered with an opalescent lavender glaze.

Ht. $2\frac{1}{8}''$ Diam. $5\frac{1}{2}''$

Chün ware

Sung Dynasty

Exhib.: OCS 1952 (Ju and Kuan), 13

Cf. Same shape:

In 'Tung ware', Percival David Foundation, A. 31

In Ju ware, Garner coll., OCS 1960 (Sung), 66, 67

In Ting ware, Kempe coll., *Ibid.*, 37

In lacquer, V. & A., *Ibid.*, 14

In lacquer inlaid with mother-of-pearl, and supporting a Chi-an tea-bowl, *Sekai Tōji Zenshu* X, Pls. 18, 60

In Koryŏ celadon, *Sekai Tōji Zenshu* XIII, Pl. 51 (lower)

In bronze, found in Six Dynasties tomb in Kweichow, *publ. Kaogu* 1959.1, p. 43

Cups on cup-stands are shown in a number of early paintings: e.g. attributed to Yen Li-pen, 'Hsiao I Trying to locate a Masterpiece', Palace Museum collection, *publ. Three Hundred Masterpieces* No. 2, here the stands are lacquer, the cups are white ware; attributed to Chang Hsüan, 'Ming Huang Playing a Flute', *Ibid.*, No. 15; attributed to Hui-tsung, but by an anonymous court painter, 'A Literary Gathering', *Ibid.*, No. 92

C. 65   Pl. 35a

Flat dish with slightly everted rim, on short, slightly splayed and bevelled foot. Stoneware. Covered with a thick, even lavender-blue glaze. An olive-brown glaze covers the base.

Ht. $1\frac{3}{4}''$ Diam. 7''
Chün ware
Sung Dynasty
Exhib.: Arts Council 1953, 24

C. 355   Pl. 35b

Bowl on small splayed foot. Grey porcellanous stoneware. Covered with a soft, opalescent and finely-crackled lavender-blue glaze. Traces of brown glaze on exposed foot.

Ht. $3\frac{7}{8}''$ Diam. 9''
Chün ware
Sung Dynasty

C. 63   Pl. 35c

Pair of shallow bowls with slightly everted rim and splayed foot. Stoneware, burnt reddish-brown where exposed. Covered with a soft lavender-blue glaze splashed inside with a zigzag in purple, and stopping outside well short of the foot in an uneven line.

Ht. $1\frac{3}{4}''$ Diam. $5\frac{1}{4}''$
Chün ware
Sung Dynasty
Exhib.: Arts Council 1953, 29

C. 45   Pl. 36a

Bowl with slightly inverted lip, standing on small splayed foot. Heavily-potted stoneware burnt reddish-brown where exposed on and near the foot. Covered with a thick green crackled glaze.

Ht. 4''   Diam. $8\frac{3}{4}''$
Green Chün ware
Sung Dynasty
Exhib.: Arts Council 1953, 40; OCS 1960 (Sung), 56

C. 66   Pl. 36b

Four-lobed vase with small slightly everted mouth, and deep concave base. Light buff stoneware, with blue-opalescent crackled glaze.

Ht. 6″   Diam. 3″

Chün ware

Sung Dynasty

Exhib.: Dartington Hall 1949, 77; OCS 1952 (Chün and Brown), 190; Arts Council 1953, 28

Cf. Similar lobed (?) Chün vase, Schoenlicht coll., BH 1935, 1110

C. 158   Pl. 37a

Shallow bowl with inverted lip, on hollow foot. Grey porcellanous stoneware, burnt reddish where exposed on the base. Covered with a thick opalescent lavender-blue glaze splashed with purple.

Ht. $1\frac{5}{8}$″   Diam. $3\frac{3}{8}$″

Chün ware

Sung Dynasty

Exhib.: BH 1935, 1095; Manchester 1936, 6448; Arts Council 1953, 25; Venice 1954, 476

C. 221   Pl. 37b

Miniature incense-burner on three short cabriole legs. Hard grey stoneware burnt red where exposed inside and on feet. Covered with a bubbly lavender glaze suffused with purple, and tending to light brown where it runs thin.

Ht. $2\frac{3}{8}$″   Diam. $2\frac{3}{4}$″

Chün ware

Sung Dynasty

Exhib.: OCS 1952 (Chün and Brown), 218; Arts Council 1953, 27

C. 247   Pl. 37c

Saucer-dish, of grey porcellanous stoneware burnt brown on exposed foot. Suggestion of fluting round the outside. Covered with a bubbly deep olive-green glaze partially crackled.

Ht. $1\frac{7}{8}$″   Diam. $7\frac{7}{8}$″

Green Chün ware

Sung Dynasty

Publ. A. L. Hetherington, *Early Chinese Wares*, p. 76 as an example of *ta-lü* ('big green'); Eumo., *Cat.* II, Pl. 18, B. 101 ('? Kuan')

Cf. Lord Cunliffe coll., Venice 1954, 470; similar dishes in the coll. of H.M. the King of Sweden, Mrs. Alfred Clark, Dr. and Mrs. H. E. Rhodes, *exhib.* at OCS 1952 (Chün and Brown), 108, 100, 103. The type is also discussed in Sir Percival David's Introduction to the *Cat.* of the Exhibition of Ju and Kuan Wares, *Trans. OCS* 1952

C. 252   Pl. 37d

Bowl with inverted rim, on rather high splayed foot. Grey stoneware covered with a soft, even, crackled lavender-blue glaze. Foot and base unglazed. Interior colour dulled; perhaps by oil.

Ht. 2″   Diam. $3\frac{1}{2}$″
Chün ware
Sung Dynasty

C. 205   Pl. 37e

Bowl with slightly inverted lip. Buff porcellanous stoneware covered with a heavily-crackled lavender-blue glaze, the crackle being stained dark. A rare and beautiful effect. The unglazed foot is burnt brown and shows traces of brown glaze.

Ht. 2″   Diam. $3\frac{7}{8}$″
Chün ware
Sung Dynasty
Exhib.: OCS 1952 (Chün and Brown), 202; Arts Council 1953, 26

C. 192   Pl. 38a

Bowl on small foot. Grey porcellanous ware, partly covered on the exposed foot-rim with a reddish-brown slip. Covered with a thick bubbly opalescent glaze, lavender-blue with three purple splashes on the outside, purple suffused here and there with cloudy blue on the inside. There is some crinkling of the glaze inside below the lip.

Ht. $3\frac{3}{4}$″   Diam. $8\frac{7}{8}$″
Chün ware
XIII–XIV century

C. 60   Pl. 38b

Bowl on hollow foot. Light grey porcellanous ware. Covered, except for the foot, with a thick, bubbly, opalescent and finely-crackled lavender-blue glaze.

Ht. $3\frac{3}{8}$″   Diam. $7\frac{1}{4}$″
Ching-te-chen Chün ware
Yüan or Ming Dynasty

C. 59   Pl. 39a

Deep bowl with slightly inverted lip, on sloping foot. Light grey porcellanous ware partly burnt brown where exposed on the foot-rim. Covered with a thick, bubbly, opalescent lavender-blue glaze. Traces of brown glaze on the base.

Ht. $3\frac{3}{8}$″   Diam. $5\frac{1}{2}$″
Chün ware
Yüan or early Ming Dynasty
Exhib.: OCS 1952 (Chün and Brown), 16; Venice 1954, 480 (another bowl is illustrated)
Cf. BH 1935, 1111 (formerly Raphael collection)

C. 251   Pl. 39b

Bottle with globular body, slightly tapering tubular neck and short foot. Porcellanous stoneware, buff where exposed on the foot-rim. Covered with a thick lightly crackled lavender-blue glaze with some greenish patches, and running down in heavy drops toward the base.

Ht. $4\frac{1}{4}''$ Diam. $3\frac{3}{4}''$
Soft Chün ware
Ming Dynasty
Cf. Eumo., *Cat.* III, Pl. 22, C. 103 ('Yüan')

C. 227   Pl. 39c

Deep bowl with slightly inverted lip, on square-cut foot. Porcellanous stoneware body covered with a thick crimson glaze having lavender-blue streaks and splashes. The glaze inside the base ranges from pale olive to dark bluish-green.

Ht. $3\frac{5}{8}''$ Diam. $7\frac{3}{4}''$
Ching-te-chen Chün ware
XIV–XV century
Exhib.: OCS 1952 (Chün and Brown), 155

C. 204   Pl. 40a

Incense-vase with globular body and wide everted mouth, standing on three heavy feet. Buff porcellanous stoneware burnt reddish where exposed; covered with a thick bluish-grey glaze streaked with purple on one side. The glaze between the feet is heavily pitted from contact with sand in the kiln.

Ht. $4\frac{1}{4}''$ Diam. $5\frac{3}{4}''$
Chün ware
Sung Dynasty or later

C. 175   Pl. 40b

Bowl with slightly inverted lip and splayed and bevelled foot. Porcelain, covered with a thick bubbly, opalescent and glassy pale lavender glaze. Brown glaze on and around exposed foot.

Ht. $2\frac{1}{8}''$ Diam. $3\frac{3}{4}''$
Ching-te-chen Chün ware
XIV–XV century

C. 32   Pl. 40c

Flower-pot, six-lobed, with straight tapering sides, and flat rim. The bottom is pierced with five drainage-holes. Heavily-potted, hard dark brown stoneware, burnt almost black on exposed foot-rim. Covered with a thick, pitted, opalescent ultramarine blue glaze suffused with lavender. Scratched on the base are the two characters Wu-hsüan[1] (Pavilion of Pleasure).

[1] See p. 157.

Ht. $5\frac{7}{8}''$ Diam. $8\frac{3}{4}''$

Probably Canton ware

Ming Dynasty

This piece has been labelled by various authorities as Sung, Ming, and XVII century,
and attributed to both Kwangtung and Ching-te-chen

6. Ting and Related Northern White Wares

The lovely white porcelain of Ting-chou was, as is well known, supplied to the Northern Sung court at Kaifeng. However, the Ting bowls had one blemish — a rough edge to the rim caused by their being fired upside-down, which had to be concealed with a metal band. The Emperor Hui-tsung, the refinement of whose taste has become legendary, evidently objected to this, for it is recorded that during the Cheng-ho era (1111–17) Ting lost its official status, and was replaced by the mysterious 'northern *kuan*'.

Chinese tradition holds that the finest Ting wares were made during the last fifty years of Northern Sung, but until recently there has been no archaeological (as opposed to literary) evidence as to when the kilns were started. Recent Chinese investigators, however, have found at the kilnsite of Chien-tz'u-ts'un near Ting-chou, shards of a typically T'ang white ware, some of which were of a kind often called Hsing-yao. Whether Chien-tz'u-ts'un will turn out to be the source of the elusive Hsing ware, however, is not yet clear. More important is the fact, revealed by this discovery, that the classic Ting ware of the Northern Sung was a development from the high quality white porcelain being made in the same area during the T'ang.

There can have been no break in the tradition. An inscribed tablet, found at Ting-chou, suggests that the kilns were already producing porcelain for the imperial household under the Five Dynasties. Confirmation of the view that Ting was already an imperial ware very shortly after the establishment of the Sung Dynasty is to be found in sources quoted in a recent article by Feng Hsien-ming.[1] The *Wu-Yüeh lüeh-shih*, Chapter 4, for example, mentions that, in the year 980, two thousand pieces of Ting ware were fitted with gold rims for the palace; fifteen years later, according to the *Sung Hui-yao chi*, there were special officials in the palace in charge of lacquer ware and of the white porcelain of Yüeh, Jao-chou (i.e. Ching-te-chen), Ting-chou and Ch'ing-chou. If this one entry is reliable, it provides the first evidence that Chekiang and Kiangsi were providing white wares for the court under the Northern Sung. The wares of Ch'ing-chou have not yet been identified.

It is often stated that at the fall of Northern Sung in 1127, the Ting potters accompanied the court in its flight southwards across the Yangtse. If Ting had ceased to be an imperial ware some ten years earlier, this would be extremely unlikely; in any case, it is based on Bushell's mistranslation of a passage in the *T'ao-shuo*. Other Western writers, allegedly quoting the *Ko-ku yao-lun*, say that the Ting potters emigrated to Chi-chou and established kilns there. While this is possible — and indeed some high quality Chi-chou porcelain with impressed or moulded designs under an ivory-white glaze clearly imitates Ting-yao — the *Ko-ku yao-lun* does not actually say so.[2]

Although the finest Northern Sung white ware of this type is all to be classed as Ting ware — a very lovely example being the conical bowl in this collection, Pl. 43a — a wide variety of imitations, including the rougher *fen* (powder) and *t'u* (earth) Ting was made not only in North China but also in Szechwan, in Kiangsi, and by the Liao potters of the

---

[1] *Wen-wu* 1959.7, pp. 67–71.

[2] See Nobumori Ozaki, 'Chinese Literature on Ceramics', *OA* (N.S.) III, 1, Spring 1957, pp. 25–27.

52

north-east. Near-Ting shards and wasters have been found at Tz'u-chou, and in the newly discovered kilns at Kuan-t'ai, Hao-pi, Yao-yao and P'ing-ting-yao, and at Chieh-hsiu-yao in Central Shansi. The incense-burner in this collection (Pl. 61c), of the same family as the pillow in the collection of Lord Cunliffe, is of a type generally called Tz'u-chou, but the discovery of very similar pieces in the Kuan-t'ai kilns suggests another possible source.

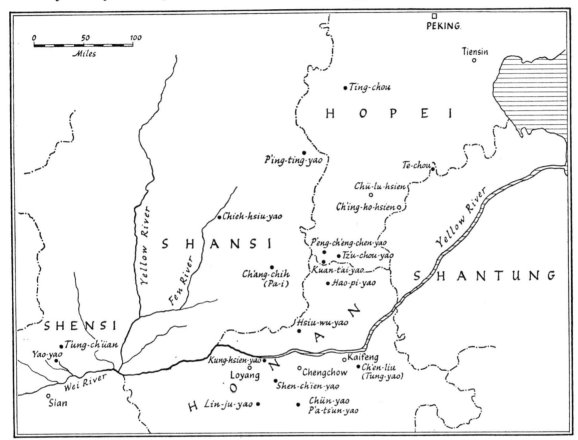

MAP II. T'ang and Sung kilns in North China

C. 178   Pl. 41

Bottle, with globular body, long neck and flanged lip, standing on a splayed base. White porcelanous ware. The body is decorated with peonies freely incised in the paste under a creamy white glaze which has a faint greenish tint where it runs thick. Hollow base, partly glazed inside.

> Ht. $10\frac{3}{4}''$ Diam. $4\frac{1}{2}''$
> Ting ware
> Sung Dynasty
> *Exhib.*: OCS 1949 (Ting, etc.), 13; Arts Council 1953, 42

C. 222   Pl. 42a

Dish, with slightly everted sloping side, of white porcelanous ware. Decorated inside with two ducks against reeds, separated by two lotus plants; three petals in the centre;

water indicated by comb-markings; all incised under a creamy-white glaze. Short foot and slightly recessed base. Rim bound in copper.

Ht. $1\frac{3}{4}''$ Diam. $8\frac{1}{4}''$
Ting ware
Sung Dynasty
Exhib.: Dartington Hall 1949, *95*; Arts Council 1953, *48*

C. 352   Pl. 42b

Flat dish with six-lobed rim, the lobes indicated by slight ridges inside and incisions outside. White translucent porcellanous ware covered with creamy white glaze with slight greenish tint where it thickens on the outside. Straight rather high foot, unglazed on the bottom of the foot-rim.

A note with this elegant dish says that it was excavated at Rayy in Persia.

Ht. $1\frac{5}{8}''$ Diam. $7\frac{7}{8}''$
Ting ware
Sung Dynasty
Exhib.: OCS 1949 (Ting, etc.), 11

C. 256   Pl. 43a

Bowl of fine white porcellanous ware. Decorated inside with flowers within a single line, incised in the paste under a creamy-white glaze with greenish tint where it thickens on the outside. Shallow square-cut foot. Edge of rim unglazed. A particularly beautiful piece.

Ht. $1\frac{3}{4}''$ Diam. $6\frac{1}{2}''$
Ting ware
Sung Dynasty
Exhib.: Arts Council 1953, *44*; Venice 1954, *536*
Publ. Eumo., *Cat.* III, Pl. 24, C. 122

C. 91   Pl. 43b

Bowl of white porcellanous ware with six-lobed rim, the lobes further indicated by incisions down the outside of the body. Decorated inside with peonies freely incised in the paste under a cream glaze which runs to thick, pale greenish-brown tear-marks on the outside and on the base. Rim unglazed. A detail of the base is shown in Plate 144a.

Ht. $2\frac{1}{2}''$ Diam. $7\frac{1}{2}''$
Ting ware
Sung Dynasty
Exhib.: OCS 1949 (Ting, etc.), 18; Arts Council 1953, *43*

C. 211   Pl. 44a

Circular box with cover, of fine-grain white porcellanous stoneware, slightly hollowed-out foot showing traces of kiln sand. Covered, except for rims of base and cover, with creamy white glaze with faint greenish tint when it runs thick. A detail of the base is shown in Plate 144d, with a fragment from the Ting kilns.

Ht. $1\frac{1}{4}''$ Diam. $3\frac{1}{2}''$
Ting ware
Sung Dynasty, X–XI century
Exhib.: OCS 1949 (Ting, etc.), 68; Arts Council 1953, 46 ('Sung'); OCS 1955, 175
('T'ang')
Cf. Schiller coll., City Art Gallery, Bristol, Venice 1954, 552 ('Sung Dynasty or
earlier'); Chinese Government coll., *publ.* Honey, *Ceramic Art of China*, Pl. 56(a)
('Sung'); BH 1935, 1279 ('Sung')

C. 62   Pl. 44b

Bowl with cover. White porcellanous ware. Lotus petals incised on the side, and on the
lid around small knob, under a creamy-white glaze which also covers the base. Centre, and
bottom of foot-rim of bowl, and underside of flange of cover, unglazed.

Ht. $2\frac{1}{2}''$ Diam. $3\frac{1}{8}''$
Ting ware. The body and glaze have some resemblance to shards brought back from
Ching-te-chen by Brankston; a southern origin cannot be ruled out
Sung Dynasty
Exhib.: Arts Council 1953, 49

C. 191   Pl. 44c

Bowl on small foot, of whitish porcellanous ware. Six lobes indicated by nicks in the rim
and slight incisions on the outside of the body. Decorated inside with water plants freely
incised in the paste under a creamy-white glaze faintly greenish where thick. Slight comb-
markings under the glaze on base. Shallow foot-rim, unglazed on the bottom.

Ht. $2\frac{5}{8}''$ Diam. $8\frac{3}{8}''$
Ting ware
Sung Dynasty
Exhib.: Musée Cernuschi 1956

C. 132   Pl. 45a

Dish of fine-grain white paste with moulded decoration. In the centre a design of lotus
plants, separated by a formalized scroll border from an outer band of peonies bounded by a
double line, covered with a creamy-white glaze. Rim and bottom of foot unglazed.

Ht. $2\frac{1}{4}''$ Diam. $11\frac{3}{4}''$
Ting ware
Sung Dynasty
Exhib.: BH 1935, 1675; OCS 1949 (Ting, etc.), 70; Arts Council 1953, 45

C. 49   Pl. 45b

Deep six-lobed bowl, the lobes indicated by incisions on the outside of the body. White
porcellanous paste. Decorated inside with lotus sprays under a creamy-white glaze with
faint greenish tinge where it thickens to tear-drops on the outside. Rim and bottom of foot-
rim unglazed. Rim bound in copper.

Ht. $3\frac{1}{4}''$ Diam. $8\frac{1}{4}''$
Ting ware
Sung Dynasty

C. 128 Pl. 46a

Bowl of heavily-potted light buff stoneware on rather high slightly splayed foot. Covered with a creamy-white crackled glaze over a white slip, the main crackle running in parallel lines across the body and stained brown. Three spur-marks inside. Traces of glaze inside roughly finished base.

Ht. $2\frac{5}{8}''$ Diam. $5\frac{5}{8}''$
North China
X–XI century
Exhib.: OCS 1960 (Sung), 110

C. 213 Pl. 46b

Small-mouthed potiche with grooved shoulder. White porcellanous ware, covered with creamy-white glaze, with faint bluish tint, which stops short of the foot-rim in an uneven line.

Ht. $1\frac{3}{4}''$ Diam. $3\frac{1}{2}''$
Ting-type ware
Sung Dynasty, X–XI century

C. 285 Pl. 46c

Box and lid of transparent sturdily-potted white porcelain with vertical quatrefoil fluted sides. Character *ho*[1] (together) incised on side of bottom and cover to indicate how they should fit. Creamy, very pale bluish-white glaze. Rims, bottom of foot and part of base unglazed.

Ht. $2\frac{5}{8}''$ Diam. $2\frac{7}{8}''$
North China
IX–XI century

C. 337 Pl. 47a

Jar with small mouth. Fine porcellanous stoneware. Vertical side divided by four hatched straps leading down to four short animal feet. Light bluish-grey glaze. Rim unglazed. Cover missing. Feet and base unglazed.

Ht. $2\frac{7}{8}''$ Diam. $3\frac{7}{8}''$
North China
IX–X century
Exhib.: OCS 1955 (T'ang), 173
Cf. Hoyt, *Cat.* 163 ('Hsing type?'); similar, but without feet, Kempe coll., Lindberg, 'Hsing-yao . . .' 99, Pl. 112 (Sung), 4; Eumo., *Cat.* III, Pl. 24, C. 116, C. 117 ('Ting ware')

[1] See p. 157.

C. 368   Pl. 47b

Jar with slightly inverted rim, square-cut foot, and flanged cover. Fine-grained porcellanous ware. A greyish slip covers the inside and most of the outside; a creamy greyish-white glaze covers outside of the lid, the upper part of the interior of the jar, and the exterior, stopping about an inch short of the foot-rim in an uneven line.

Ht. $3\frac{1}{2}''$ Diam. $3\frac{7}{8}''$
North China
IX–X century

C. 369   Pl. 48a

Dish with flanged side and everted rim, of white porcelain. Decorated inside with lotus spray, freely incised in the paste under a slightly crackled greyish-white glaze with a faint greenish tint. Rim and bottom of shallow foot-rim unglazed.

Ht. $1\frac{3}{4}''$ Diam. $7\frac{1}{4}''$
North China
Sung Dynasty

C. 228   Pl. 48b

Bowl on small foot, of rather heavy white porcelain. Decorated inside with flower spray incised in the paste under a creamy Ting-type glaze, slightly pitted. Rim and chamfered foot-rim unglazed.

Ht. $3''$ Diam. $8''$
North China
XI–XIII century

7. Sung Dynasty Black-glazed Wares of North China

The Northern black-glazed stonewares belong to the huge Tz'u-chou family, and many of them were made in the kilns discussed under that heading. They are here placed in a separate category simply for convenience.

It has sometimes been thought that the 'Honan *temmoku*' originated in an attempt to imitate Fukien *temmoku*. While this is probably true of some of the tea-bowls with hare's fur (Pl. 54a) or oilspot (Pl. 53b) marking, the North China black tradition certainly goes back to the T'ang Dynasty: the three splendid pieces in this collection covered with a black glaze with purplish-white suffusion (Pls. 19a & c, Colour Pl. C) are clearly T'ang ancestors of the splashed Chün wares. The Northern Sung also saw the development of a rich lustrous black glaze, the elegant little vase (Pl. 50b) being a peculiarly perfect specimen. Spotted effects (Pl. 52c) were produced by bubbles in the glaze rising to the surface and bursting there.

The discovery of the Hao-pi kilns (discussed under Tz'u-chou wares) has localized at least one source of these wares. Black tea-bowls with creamy-white rim were made there, also black vases with vertical ribbing the edge of which is light brown, a type represented by a beautiful vase in the collection of Mrs. Alfred Clark. The handsome bowl in this collection (Pl. 50a) with light brown radiating lines in a glossy black glaze, may also have been made at the Hao-pi kilns, which were active into the Yüan Dynasty. A black ware was also made at Chieh-hsiu-yao in central Shansi. The tradition is still flourishing in North China today.

C. 334 Pl. 49a
Conical bowl with vertical rim, on a square-cut foot. Roughly potted light buff stoneware covered with a lustrous black 'orange peel' glaze splashed with rust-brown and ending outside half-way down the body in broad sweeps.

Ht. $3\frac{1}{4}''$ Diam. $7\frac{3}{8}''$
Cf. BM, formerly Eumorfopoulos coll. *exhib.* BH 1935, 1211

C. 114 Pl. 49b
Jar with ovoid body and small grooved neck. Buff stoneware, covered with a lustrous black glaze decorated with two simplified birds (possibly cranes) in rust-brown, executed in broad brushstrokes.

Ht. $7\frac{3}{8}''$ Diam. $6\frac{3}{4}''$
Exhib.: OCS 1952 (Chün and Brown), 84; Arts Council 1953, 30
Cf. Lord Cunliffe coll., OCS 1960 (Sung), 75; Eumo., *Cat.* II, Pl. 72, B. 282; Venice 1954, 506; Hoyt, *Cat.* 310, 311 ('Tz'u-chou ware, XIII–XIV century')

C. 312 Pl. 50a
Bowl on slightly splayed foot, light buff stoneware, covered with a thick lustrous black

58

glaze over a thin underglaze of olive-brown, both stopping short of the foot. Inside the black is striped with radiating purplish-brown lines in imitation of the rare 'black Ting', while outside it runs down to heavy drops, the lowest of which have picked up an accretion of kiln-sand.

Ht. $3\frac{3}{8}''$ Diam. $8\frac{1}{8}''$
Probably made at Hao-pi, Honan
Cf. Eumo., *Cat.* II, Pl. LXVII, B. 276

C. 162   Pl. 50b

Baluster vase with ovoid body, slender neck and flaring foliate mouth, standing on a high splayed base. Light buff stoneware, covered with a lustrous black glaze. A particularly elegant little piece.

Ht. $6\frac{1}{2}''$ Diam. $2\frac{3}{4}''$
Exhib.: OCS 1952 (Chün and Brown), 50; Arts Council 1953, 32
Publ. Eumo., *Cat.* II, Pl. LXXII, B. 297; Honey, *Ceramic Art*, Pl. 54A

C. 384   Pl. 51a

Shallow bowl with slightly everted rim, on square-cut shallow foot. Light grey porcellanous ware, covered with a thick lustrous black glaze with brown splashes, partly covering the foot. Round the rim is a band of rich creamy-white glaze.

Ht. $2''$ Diam. $4\frac{5}{8}''$

C. 88   Pl. 51b

Shallow conical bowl on a small square-cut base. Light buff porcellanous stoneware covered with lustrous brownish-black glaze stopping unevenly short of the foot. The rim is covered with a band of creamy-white glaze.

Ht. $1\frac{3}{4}''$ Diam. $5\frac{7}{8}''$
Possibly from Hao-pi, Honan
Cf. Eumo., *Cat.* II, B. 301, where Hobson noted that bowls of this type were still being made at P'eng-ch'eng, in the Tz'u-chou district

C. 289   Pl. 51c

Shallow bowl with inverted rim on a wide shallow foot. Greyish-white porcellanous ware, covered with a dark brownish-black glaze with five reddish-brown iron splashes on the inside. The glaze stops irregularly short of the rim which has an unevenly applied cream glaze. The bottom of the foot-rim is unglazed, but the base is partially glazed inside.

Ht. $2''$ Diam. $5\frac{1}{4}''$
XII–XIII century

C. 218a   Pl. 52a

Jar with body rounded below and splayed above, with everted and foliated rim, on straight-cut slightly splayed foot. Coarse light buff sandy stoneware covered with a rich reddish-brown glaze which stops short of the bottom, both inside and out, in a sweeping line.

Ht. $3\frac{1}{2}''$ Diam. $4\frac{7}{8}''$

X–XI century

Exhib.: Arts Council 1953, 37 ('Northern black ware')

Cf. Similar jar but on higher foot, with cream glaze, in Hoyt, *Cat.* 151 ('Late T'ang');
V. & A., *publ.* Eumo., *Cat.* II, Pl. 64; Honey, *The Art of the Potter*, Pl. 14b; Honey,
The Ceramic Art of China, Pl. 54c ('Sung or earlier, perhaps T'ang'); lobed jar of
this type, Eumo., *Cat.* II, Pl. 55, B. 254 ('Honan type')

C. 64   Pl. 52b

Bowl with upright rim on a small square-cut foot. Light buff stoneware, covered with a
black glaze with hare's fur markings inside and streaked with reddish-brown patches, and
with a pool of thick black glaze in the bottom. The glaze stops well short of the foot in a
sweeping line.

Ht. $2\frac{3}{4}''$ Diam. 7″

Exhib.: BH 1935, 1211; OCS 1952 (Chün and Brown), 120; Arts Council 1953, 33

C. 115   Pl. 52c

Shallow bowl on low chamfered foot. Coarse opaque buff porcelain covered with a thick
black glaze spotted with brown bubble-bursts, and stopping short of the base in an irregular
line. A fine specimen of 'oil-spot' glaze.

Ht. $1\frac{3}{8}''$ Diam. $4\frac{5}{8}''$

C. 324   Pl. 53a

Bowl with everted rim, square-cut foot and shallow base. Light buff stoneware covered
with a brownish-black glaze with purplish-brown iron-spots over a blackish slip probably
applied to simulate a Chien body. The glaze ends irregularly above the foot.

Ht. 2″   Diam. $4\frac{3}{4}''$

C. 138   Pl. 53b

Bowl with slightly inverted rim, on square-cut foot. Whitish stoneware covered with a
golden-brown underglaze, over which is a thick blue-black flecked with irregular silvery
iridescent 'oil-spots'. The glaze stops short of the base in an uneven line.

Ht. $2\frac{7}{8}''$ Diam. 6″

C. 282   Pl. 53c

Shallow conical bowl on a square-cut foot and very shallow base. Fine-grained light buff
porcellanous stoneware rather finely-potted and covered with a lustrous black glaze with
rust splashes inside and large areas of rust outside, stopping unevenly round the foot.

Ht. $1\frac{3}{4}''$ Diam. $5\frac{7}{8}''$

Exhib.: OCS 1952 (Chün and Brown), 130; OCS 1960 (Sung), 70

C. 11   Pl. 54a

Conical bowl with everted lip and short slightly rounded foot. Porcellanous stoneware covered with a thick brownish-black 'hare's fur' glaze which stops unevenly around the foot. Two little splashes of glaze inside the shallow base.

Ht. $2\frac{1}{2}''$ Diam. $5\frac{3}{8}''$

Possibly made in imitation of Chien *temmoku,* but its northern origin is shown by its light body, small foot and delicate potting.

C. 241 Pl. 54b

Bowl on small square-cut foot. Light greyish delicately-potted porcellanous ware, covered with a brownish-black glaze, with large reddish-brown iron patches; the glaze runs unevenly down over the base, which is glazed inside.

Ht. $2\frac{1}{2}''$ Diam. $6\frac{7}{8}''$

C. 30 Pl. 54c

Ovoid jar, with short grooved neck and two pairs of loop-handles on the shoulder, one of which has been repaired with gold lacquer; short, fairly wide and slightly splayed foot. Stoutly-potted buff stoneware, with a thick black lustrous glaze. Apparently a thick black glaze was first applied over the upper portion; the whole vessel was then covered with a thinner black glaze, the bottom of the foot being subsequently wiped clean. On the upper half of the vessel the outer glaze has developed an irregular crackle, through which the underglaze has oozed forming a pattern of minute lead-grey ridges. The interior is also glazed and crackled.

Ht. $9\frac{1}{2}''$ Diam. $8\frac{7}{8}''$

Probably Sung Dynasty

Exhib.: OCS 1952 (Sung), 31; Arts Council 1953, 31

Publ. Hetherington and Hobson, *The Art of the Chinese Potter,* Pl. XC ('Tz'u-chou ware, XV century')

C. 163 Pl. 55a

Conical tea-bowl with vertical rim, on very high small foot. Coarse buff stoneware covered with a lustrous variegated glaze ranging from light brown to purplish-black, and patterned with radiating streaks of russet-brown. The foot-rim and hollow base are un-glazed, and there is an accretion of kiln-sand in the base.

Ht. $2\frac{5}{8}''$ Diam. $4\frac{3}{8}''$

The rough potting at first suggests Chi-chou ware, but the light high-fired paste and small delicate foot are more characteristic of North China

Publ. Trans. OCS 1937–38, Pl. 2; Eumo., *Cat.* II, Pl. 88, B. 230

C. 127 Pl. 55b

Shallow conical bowl with slightly everted lip, on small square-cut foot with five sand-marks on the bottom. Thinly-potted porcellanous stoneware, covered with a lustrous glaze flecked with purplish iron spots. Glazed inside the base.

Ht. $1\frac{5}{8}''$ Diam. $5''$

Exhib.: BH 1935, 1152; Manchester 1936, 6449; OCS 1952 (Chün and Brown), 124

C. 330   Pl. 55c

Conical bowl with everted lip and small slightly splayed foot. Whitish stoneware covered with a lustrous black glaze flecked with rust spots inside and chiefly rust-brown outside, stopping above the foot in a straight line.

On the base are written three characters in faded black ink, of which the first seems to be the family name Wang; the others may be Yüan-yin.[1]

Ht. $1\frac{7}{8}''$ Diam. $4\frac{7}{8}''$

[1] See p. 157

8. Tz'u-Chou Wares of the Sung and Yüan Dynasties

The term 'Tz'u-chou ware' is a convenient misnomer. Like 'Swatow ware', it covers a whole ceramic family, made over a wide area and a long period of time. Some recent Chinese writers refer to it as 'North China people's ware' in contradistinction to the classic wares of Ting, Ju and Chün, but in fact it embraces only the stonewares decorated with black or white glaze, or those with painted, reserved or sgraffito designs, and the small class decorated with green and red enamels over the glaze. The importance of these wares in the history of Chinese ceramics lies not merely in the freedom and beauty of their decoration, but also in the fact that for the first time they employed the techniques of underglaze and overglaze painting which, in the Ming Dynasty, were to be developed with such brilliant effect in the decoration of porcelain.

Tz'u-chou wares have long been ignored by Chinese connoisseurs for their lack of refinement, and the Chinese Government sent not a single piece to Burlington House in 1935, nor, for that matter, were any specimens included among the palace treasures sent from Taiwan for exhibition in the United States in 1961–62. On the other hand, a great deal of study and investigation of them has been carried out in China itself since 1950, not, it should be said, because the eyes of the Chinese were opened to their beauty by Western enthusiasts, but because they are a true 'people's ware', displaying all the vitality of a popular ceramic tradition.

During the last ten years many kilnsites, in addition to those at Tz'u-chou, have been discovered in North China. During the winter of 1957–58, for example, kilns were located at Kuan-t'ai, near Han-tan on the Hopei–Honan border; although the excavations were rather hastily carried out, the survey team identified six strata, of which the third, fourth and fifth deposits contained a mass of material datable, by inscribed shards and coins, between the beginning and the end of Northern Sung. All the main Tz'u-chou types seem to have been made there. The few pieces so far published include a jar with a floral spray painted in black on white similar to the beautiful pieces in this collection (Pls. 56a & b), and a white glazed lamp in the form of a lion with a bowl on its back, which appears from a small photograph to be of the same general type as the bowl supported on four lions (Pl. 61c).

Tz'u-chou wares were made at a number of kilns in Honan. Some of the finest jars and vases with floral designs boldly carved through a black glaze, or reserved on black, were made at Hsiu-wu (also called Chiao-tso and Tang-yang-yü) in the foothills between the north bank of the Yellow River and the Shansi border. Kilns at Teng-feng-hsien, southeast of Loyang, produced carved sgraffito wares (Shen-chi'en-yao); rather coarse types were made in the village of P'a-ts'un, in Yü-hsien.

Four kilnsites were discovered in 1952 at Hao-pi in T'ang-yin-hsien, south of Anyang, and investigated two years later. They lie in and around the villages of Ch'en-chia-ts'un, Ting-tzu-kou, Kuan-tzu-p'o and Teng-chia-ts'un. At the largest kilns in Ch'en-chia-ts'un, six types have been identified: a thin-bodied ware, chiefly small bowls, with carved designs under a white glaze; a white ware, including big dishes, with birds and flowers boldly painted in black (similar, but not so lively, painted wares were found at P'a-ts'un); a white ware with designs of fishes and weeds painted in reddish-brown, very like those made at the Kuan-t'ai kilns just across the border in Hopei; big and small bowls glazed black inside and white outside, or black with a white rim (Pl. 51b); a black ware, chiefly jars and bottles, with yellowish-brown lines, like the famous *mei-p'ing* in the collection of Mrs. Alfred Clark; and finally, large storage jars and dishes made for daily use, with birds, animal and flower designs freely carved under a yellow or yellowish-brown glaze — a tradition that has survived in North China until today.

In Shensi, kilns at Huang-pao-chen near T'ung-ch'üan (formerly T'ung-kuan) produced Tz'u-chou type wares in addition to their main output of 'northern celadon'.

In Shansi, kilns at Chieh-hsiu-yao, discovered in 1957, turned out a wide variety of Tz'u-chou wares, in addition to northern celadon with moulded designs.

Kilns in Po-hsiang-hsien in Shantung are said to have produced a painted ware called Po-hsiang yao, but they have not yet been located.

In Kiangsu, painted wares were made at Pai-t'u-chen in Hsiao-hsien.

In Szechwan, a provincial imitation of Tz'u-chou ware was made in the Liu-li-ch'ang kilns outside the South Gate of Chengtu.

The beautiful bowls with flowers swiftly sketched in red and green over a creamy glaze, of which Pl. 64c is a typical specimen, are the earliest known enamelled wares of China. Three sources for them have now been found: in Honan, at P'a-ts'un in Yü-hsien, not far from the Ju kilns; in Shansi, at Pa-i near Ch'ang-chih, which also made heavily-potted jars with designs cut through the glaze of the type of Pl. 61a; and in Shantung at Te-chou on the Hopei border north of Chinan.

The dating of these northern painted stonewares presents something of a problem. None of them seems to be earlier than the tenth century, while the Tz'u-chou tradition has kept its vigour till modern times, and is still very much alive. But there are pointers in the case of certain kilns. A general consistency of style among the Hsiu-wu wares, for instance, suggests a limited period of production; the enamelled bowls of P'a-ts'un, Pa-i and Te-chou were being made before the end of the Sung Dynasty, and remained popular through the Yüan, especially in the far north; the stratified kilnsite at Kuan-t'ai shows evidence of a sharp decline after the end of Northern Sung; the Hao-pi kilns continued in production under the Chin and Yüan Dynasties.

It has been noted that among the quantities of North China wares found in tombs of the Liao Dynasty in Manchuria, which included Ting, *ch'ing-pai* and celadon, no Tz'u-chou were found. This has led one recent Chinese authority to suggest that they were not being manufactured until after the fall of the Liao Dynasty in 1125. But there is abundant evidence to the contrary, and the explanation may simply be that the Liao people had no need to import pottery of a type and quality they could perfectly well make themselves.

C. 329   Pl. 56a

Ovoid jar of light buff stoneware with rim slightly thickened on the inside, and short foot. Covered with a creamy-white slip applied very thick and running to tear-drops, and stopping well short of the base. Boldly painted over the slip with three sprays of foliage in thick brownish-black pigment under a transparent glaze. The design is identical with that on Pl. 56b and was probably painted by the same potter.

Ht. $4\frac{1}{2}''$ Diam. $5\frac{1}{2}''$
Possibly from the Kuan-t'ai kilns
Sung Dynasty
Exhib.: Arts Council 1953, 16

C. 179A   Pl. 56b

Vase (*mei-p'ing*) with short neck and flanged lip, slightly flaring foot and recessed base. Coarse buff stoneware, exquisitely painted with three sprays of foliage in thick, almost black, pigment over a thick creamy-white slip which stops unevenly round the base. Unglazed.

Ht. $9\frac{3}{4}''$ Diam. $4\frac{1}{2}''$
Possibly from the Kuan-t'ai kilns
Sung Dynasty
Exhib.: OCS 1949 (Ting, etc.), 177; Arts Council 1953, 19; Musée Cernuschi 1956
Cf. OCS 1960 (Sung), 98

C. 362   Pl. 57a

Pillow in the form of a couchant lion with crossed paws and thoughtful expression, modelled in heavily-potted light grey buff stoneware, and covered with an uneven crackled cream glaze applied over a white slip. A panel on his back is decorated with floral scrolls within a broad border painted in brown slip under the glaze. The eyes are also picked out in brown.

Ht. $5\frac{1}{2}''$ L. $13''$
Made in imitation of Ting ware[1]
Sung Dynasty

C. 203   Pl. 57b

Shallow bowl on a small foot. Light buff stoneware covered with a white slip and decorated inside with lotus flowers and leaves boldly incised through the slip against hatched background, the whole then covered with a transparent glaze. The rim is bound in copper, there are five spur-marks in the bottom, and the glaze and slip are finished unevenly round the foot.

Ht. $2\frac{1}{2}''$ Diam. $8\frac{1}{4}''$
Sung Dynasty
Exhib.: OCS 1949 (Sung), 155; Arts Council 1953, 20; Venice 1954, 518; OCS 1960
   (Sung), 91
Cf. Similar bowl with flowers against hatched background, *Sekai Tōji Zenshu* X,
   p. 231, fig. 113; Hoyt, *Cat.* 269

[1] For an example of the type of Ting pillow which this specimen is emulating, see Jean Gordon Lee, 'A Slip-decorated Ting Pillow in the Philadelphia Museum of Art, and Some Related Pieces', *FECB* XII, 1–2 (June–December 1960), 11–14.

C. 202   Pl. 58a

Bowl with slightly everted rim on short straight foot. Light buff stoneware much discoloured. Covered with a white slip on which an inscription of nineteen characters in four columns is written inside in brownish-black with a triple ring round the rim, covered with a transparent glaze which on the outside drips down unevenly.

Inside is the following inscription written in iron-brown glaze:

Sheng Sung erh nien cheng yüeh chih wang feng Ch'un
        weng lao she-chang
K'an-tsao yü Chün-chou

'The fifteenth of January in the second year
    of the Imperial Sung [A.D. 961]
For Old Mr. Ch'un, the village headman
Made in Chün-chou'

It is unusual to find the year inscribed thus instead of with the customary *nien-hao*, but a possible explanation is that the potter knew that the new dynasty had been established but did not yet know what the *nien-hao* was. The Chün-chou referred to here is not the one which produced the famous Chün ware, but an as yet unidentified factory in North China *She-chang* could also mean the head of a club or society of some sort.

If this bowl is an authentic Sung piece, it is of considerable interest as showing that there was already a factory turning out 'Tz'u-chou type' pottery at the beginning of Northern Sung. However it is possible that while the bowl itself is early, the inscription may have been fired on at a later date.

Ht. 2⅜″   Diam. 7½″
Sung Dynasty
Exhib.: Arts Council 1953, 21

C. 239   Pl. 58b

Jar with globular body and short neck, on high foot with slightly recessed base, ornamented with five rows of grooved 'petals' looped back over the body suggesting the lotus. Buff stoneware, covered with a colourless glaze over a creamy-white slip, stopping unevenly round the base. The inside has splashes of white slip under the colourless glaze.

The 'lotus petals' suggest that this type may have been intended for Buddhist funeral ceremonies.

Ht. 5⅛″   Diam. 6⅝″
Sung Dynasty
Exhib.: Berlin 1929, 643; OCS 1949 (Ting, etc.), 182 ('Probably Sung, Tz'u-chou');
        Arts Council 1953, 18
Cf. A pair of very similar jars in Laurence Sickman coll., mysteriously labelled 'pickle
        jar', Los Angeles 1952, 247; Kempe coll., *Kinas Kunst i Svensk og Dansk Eje*
        (Chinese Art in Swedish and Danish Collections), Copenhagen, 1950, Pl. XX
        ('Ch'ing-ho-hsien, Ting-yao')

C. 306   Pl. 59

Vase (*mei-p'ing*) with elongated ovoid body, short neck and flaring lip, and short square-cut foot. Light buff stoneware. Covered with a white slip, which ends unevenly around the foot, and covers the inside of the base. The decoration, which is carved and incised through the slip, is divided by horizontal bands into four zones. Round the neck is a band of lotus leaves, below this a broad zone of peony scrolls, then more lotus-leaves (?), the lowest zone containing ogee-shaped lines suggesting formalized petals. The vessel is covered with a crackled almost colourless glaze through which the body shows with a light bluish-grey tint. The neck and lip have been restored.

Ht. $14\frac{1}{2}''$ Diam. $7\frac{5}{8}''$
Sung Dynasty
Exhib.: BH 1935, 1240; New Zealand 1936, 153A; OCS 1949 (Ting, etc.), 188; Dartington Hall 1949, 100
Cf. Eumo., *Cat.* III, Pl. LXXIII, C. 391

C. 365   Pl. 60a

Ovoid bottle with short neck and thickened lip, with two ribbed handles on the shoulder. Heavily-potted buff stoneware. Ornamented with swiftly sketched floral sprays and one illegible character painted in rich purplish-brown over an olive-green 'tea dust' glaze. The shallow base is also glazed and there is a little accretion of kiln-sand round the foot.

Ht. $10\frac{3}{4}''$ Diam. $6\frac{3}{4}''$
Sung Dynasty
Exhib.: OCS 1952 (Chün and Brown), 63; OCS 1960 (Sung), 76
Cf. Hoyt, *Cat.* 303

C. 296   Pl. 60b

Tall ovoid jar with small mouth, flattened everted rim and thick splayed foot. Light grey stoneware, covered with white slip and finely-crackled creamy-white glaze, both of which stop short of the base in uneven lines. Stained brown on one side.

Ht. $9\frac{7}{8}''$ Diam. $4\frac{3}{4}''$
Probably from Chü-lu-hsien
Sung Dynasty
Exhib.: Arts Council 1953, 15; OCS 1960 (Sung), 109

C. 150   Pl. 60c

Bowl with everted rim, on a short square-cut foot. Light buff stoneware burnt red where exposed. Covered with a creamy-white slip which stops well short of the base. In the bottom three concentric rings in dark grey-brown. The rim is decorated with dark blobs, with a thick border on the outside above two thinner bands. The inside and part of the outside are covered with an almost transparent glaze through which the dark slip shows a smoky blue-grey, whereas the exposed dark slip outside is reddish-brown.

Ht. $2\frac{1}{2}''$ Diam. $6''$
Sung Dynasty

C. 166   Pl. 61a

Jar with ovoid body and short straight neck, on a short splayed and bevelled foot. Covered with a thick treacly black glaze which has been carved away leaving in relief a bold design of two bands of floral scrolls; round the neck a band of scalloping. The glaze stops an inch short of the base in a straight line. The interior is glazed.

Ht. $8\frac{1}{8}''$ Diam. $10\frac{7}{8}''$

Made in Shansi

XII–XIII century

Exhib.: Arts Council 1953, 22 ('Sung')

Publ. Eumo., *Cat.* III, Pl. LIX, C. 419 ('Tz'u-chou type, Sung or Yüan')

Cf. Also Eumo., *Cat.* III, Pl. LIX, C. 413, C. 423; H.M. the King of Sweden coll., *Cat.* Pl. 93; similar vessels made in Shansi, Ch'en Wan-li, *Sung tai pei-fang min-chien tz'u-ch'i* (Northern People's Ceramics of the Sung Dynasty), Pls. 32, 33

C. 389   Pl. 61b

Wine-cup and stand. White stoneware, covered with finely-crackled cream glaze, decorated with reddish-brown iron-spots suggesting flowers.

Total ht. $1\frac{3}{4}''$ Diam. of cup $2\frac{1}{2}''$ Diam. of stand $2\frac{3}{4}''$

Sung Dynasty

C. 367   Pl. 61c

Incense-burner in the form of a bowl on high, hollow splayed foot. The bowl is supported on four crouching lions, and decorated with lotus leaves carved in the white paste. Roughly made and finished. Covered with a faintly-crackled cream glaze.

Ht. $4\frac{1}{8}''$ Diam. $4\frac{3}{8}''$

Possibly from the Kuan-t'ai kilns, and close to Ting ware

Sung Dynasty, X–XII century

Cf. Pillow in the coll. of Lord Cunliffe, OCS 1949 (Ting, etc.), 178, and OCS 1960 (Sung), 100 ('Tz'u-chou'); lion excavated from Kuan-t'ai kilns, *publ. Wen-wu* 1959.6, 58–61

C. 176   Pl. 62a

Baluster vase with straight neck and everted foliated rim, standing on a broad foot. Hard buff pottery, covered with a white slip and decorated round the shoulder with foliage sprays, simply drawn in dark brown under a colourless crackled glaze. The deep conical base is unglazed and carries a date written in faded ink. It runs *?-yu shih-i nien cheng yüeh ch'u*,[1] 'Early January of the eleventh year of — *yu*'. The first character of the *nien-hao* is illegible. There are ten reign periods between 948 (Later Han) and 1314 (Yüan) which have this character *yu* as the second element.

Ht. $8\frac{1}{8}''$ Diam. $3\frac{1}{2}''$

Sung Dynasty, probably XII–XIII century

[1] See p. 157.

C. 350   Pl. 62b

Pear-shaped vase with slender neck and flaring lip, on short splayed and bevelled foot. Buff stoneware burnt reddish-brown where exposed. Decorated over a white slip with very sketchily drawn floral sprays below a band of vertical blobs between double lines, painted in dull reddish-brown slip under a tea-dust greenish-brown glaze. This shape is found in Yüan metalwork.

Ht. $12\frac{3}{8}''$ Diam. $7''$
XIII–XIV century
Exhib.: OCS 1960 (Sung), 90
Cf. Pl. 60a of this coll.

C. 28   Pl. 62c

Saucer dish, with slightly everted and thickened lip, on sharply-cut and bevelled foot. Buff stoneware. A thick black glaze has been applied round the rim inside and out, so as to leave a curving-sided pentagon of bare paste covered with white slip, within which six foliage sprays have been sketched in thick droplets of black glaze. Outside, the glaze also stops below the lip, forming a pentagon.

Ht. $1\frac{1}{4}''$ Diam. $6\frac{1}{2}''$
X or XI century
Cf. Eumo., *Cat.* II, B. 291, p. 49 and Pl. 71

C. 338   Pl. 63a

Ovoid jar with wide mouth and short straight neck. Heavily-potted stoneware burnt reddish where exposed on the shallow base. Covered with a creamy-white glaze, and decorated in brown with a four-clawed dragon chasing a flaming pearl and a phoenix, amid clouds between horizontal bands, painted in dark brown, with lines swiftly sketched through the brown to the white glaze beneath. Glazed brownish-black inside. The unglazed rim has been broken and repaired.

Ht. $12\frac{1}{4}''$ Diam. $14\frac{1}{4}''$
XIII–XIV century
Exhib.: Arts Council 1953, 17

C. 333A   Pl. 63b

Jar with short neck and wide mouth, thick flat foot and deeply recessed base. Heavily-potted hard grey stoneware burnt reddish-brown where exposed on foot-rim and inside base. Covered with a white slip and decorated with two sprawling phoenixes amid clouds in ogival panels, crudely drawn in dark brown pigment, with lines scratched through to the slip; covered with a transparent glaze. The inside is covered with a thick black and brown *temmoku*-type glaze; and there are five spur-marks on the bottom.

Ht. $7\frac{5}{8}''$ Diam. $8\frac{3}{8}''$
XIII–XIV century
Exhib.: Burlington Fine Arts Club 1910, Pl. 28, D. 1
Publ. Honey, *Ceramic Art of China*, Pl. 73B ('Sung or later')

C. 183   Pl. 64a

Bottle with straight side, sloping shoulder, small neck and everted mouth, on a flat base slightly recessed in concentric rings. Hard greyish-white porcellanous stoneware covered with a white slip, and decorated in brown under a transparent glaze. The body is adorned with fishes and a bird amid lotuses; round the shoulder, between a band of scroll-work and a band of twisted ribbon pattern is an inscription of four characters separated by wavy lines. It reads *chiu ch'i ch'ung t'ien*,[1] 'may the vapour of the wine fill the heavens'.

Ht. $7\frac{3}{4}''$ Diam. $6\frac{3}{4}''$

XIII–XIV century

C. 308   Pl. 64b

Bottle with pear-shaped body, long slender neck and everted rim, on a short slightly splayed foot. Yellowish buff poor-quality stoneware, covered with a thick white slip. The decoration in two zones consists of a broad band with two phoenixes amid prunus and a narrow band of prunus, bordered by triple and quadruple lines, sketched in brown under a colourless glaze.

Ht. $11\frac{3}{4}''$ Diam. $6''$

XIV century

C. 149   Pl. 64c

Bowl on short straight-cut foot. Buff stoneware, covered with a thin slip and a creamy-white finely-crackled glaze both of which stop well short of the foot in an uneven line. Decorated inside with bold pattern of peony flowers and leaves painted in red and green enamel within a border of four red lines. Five spur-marks in the bottom.

Koyama notes two bowls of this type, with dates equivalent to 1201 and 1230 written in ink on the bottom.[2] Many fragments of this ware have been found in Yüan sites in Mongolia, suggesting that it was popular for a long time north of the Great Wall.

This piece is unusual in that the decoration is contemporary with the bowl and not, as is often the case, a later addition.

Ht. $2\frac{1}{8}''$ Diam. $6\frac{1}{8}''$

Probably made at Yü-hsien in Honan, or Pa-i in Shansi

Late Sung or Yüan Dynasty

Exhib.: Dartington Hall 1949, 105; Arts Council 1953, 23; Musée Cernuschi 1956

Cf. Bowls in private Japanese collections, *Sekai Tōji Zenshu* X, Pls. 122, 123, 124, 125; Seattle Art Museum, Los Angeles 1952, 253; Art Institute of Chicago, Los Angeles, 254

[1] See p. 157.
[2] Koyama Fujio, *Sekai Tōji Zenshu* X, 14.

9. Northern Celadon Ware of the Sung Dynasty

Until recently this ware has been known in China as Lin-ju-yao, because kilns that produced it were long ago located in Lin-ju-hsien (fifty miles south of Loyang), the source also of Ju ware. The recent discovery of other factories where it was made, however, has now rendered this name obsolete, or at least ambiguous. Nevertheless, the term 'northern celadon' is both apt and convenient, for there are good grounds for the view that it was made by, or influenced by, Chekiang potters who came north to Honan with the establishment of the Sung capital at Kaifeng. In shape, techniques of decoration, and glaze colour, it is intimately related to the finest tenth- and eleventh-century Yüeh, as is illustrated by the important ewer (Pl. 73). This vessel has been attributed both to Honan and to Chekiang, and though here given to Chekiang by reason of the treatment of the loop-handles, which is exactly paralleled in the Yüeh vase (Pl. 75a), there is still room for doubt.

While the finest northern celadons were probably those produced at Lin-ju-hsien, very similar though not so fine wares, with impressed or incised decoration under an olive-green glaze, were made at the recently discovered kilns in the small mountain village of Huang-pao-chen, about forty miles north of Sian. The kilns lie in the district of Yao-hsien, hence the name Yao-yao. In the *Fang-chih*, the site is called Shih-li yao-ch'ang, because the kilns extended for ten *li* along the hillside. They all produced a northern celadon, decorated with incised or impressed designs under a glaze that is lighter, thinner and often more gingery-yellow than that of Lin-ju-hsien. The kilns are mentioned in several sources. The *T'ao-lu*, for example, says that 'in making celadon, they imitated Ju, but the ware could not compare with it in colour and quality'. The *Lao-hsüeh-an pi-chi* by the Sung Poet Lu Yu notes, significantly, that the celadon of Yao-yao resembles in colour the *pi-se* (secret colour) ware of Yü-yao hsien, 'therefore it is called Yüeh-yao, though it is coarse and not so good. So only the eating-houses use it as it lasts longer.' The *Ch'ing-p'o tsa-chih* (1132) states that the white is the best quality — though recent Chinese investigators failed to find any shards of white ware. 'In modern times', this source notes, 'people say that they imitated Ting. The body is very thin, but thicker than Ting. The colour, although white and delicate, is slightly yellowish when compared with Ting. The ware has *an-hua* decoration of phoenix and peonies.' The best products of this factory must have been of high quality, for the *Sung-shih* (Official History of the Sung Dynasty) says that Yao-yao sent tribute to court.

A tablet found in the kitchen of the village school at Huang-pao-chen proved that pottery was already being made there in 1068. On the basis of shards picked up along the hillside, Chinese investigators concluded that the quality of the Huang-pao-chen ware was not as high as that of the celadon of Lin-ju-hsien. They notice that the rougher wares were stacked in the kiln and consequently have an unglazed ring in the bottom.

Kilns producing northern celadon have been discovered in recent years at Chieh-hsiu-yao in central Shansi, and at Pao-feng-yao in Honan, seventy miles south-south-east of Loyang.

When a new kilnsite is discovered, it is always tempting to attribute to it puzzling pieces in Western collections, but any such correlation must be extremely tentative unless one has the opportunity to compare the latter with actual specimens from the kilns. All we can say of the pieces in this collection is that two bowls (Pl. 67b & c) seem to correspond closely in shape and decoration to descriptions of excavated pieces from Yao-yao; the conical bowl (Pl. 66c), with its gingery yellowish-green glaze might be a coarse product of the kilns; and the little incense-burner (Pl. 68c) one of the finer pieces which come close to Ju; it resembles two specimens unearthed at Ch'ien-hsien, which the author of the monograph from which I have quoted identifies as Yao-yao. The large bowl (Pl. 141c) which has been widely exhibited as a specimen of northern celadon, conforms to the Yao-yao criteria in glaze colour and in having an unglazed ring in the bottom. In other aspects, however, it seems to stand apart from the Sung northern celadon as a whole and must remain a problem piece.

C. 81 Pl. 65a

Six-lobed dish with flaring lip standing on a low foot, of light grey stoneware. Decorated inside with a carved design of peonies under an olive-green glaze. The upper half of the exterior is decorated with swiftly cut vertical incisions. The foot is sharply cut, with kiln sand adhering to the inside. The bottom of the foot-rim is unglazed and burnt reddish-grey. The base is glazed inside.

An exceptionally fine specimen.

Ht. $1\frac{7}{8}''$ Diam. $7\frac{3}{4}''$

Exhib.: BH 1935, 1685; Manchester 1936, 278; OCS 1947 (Celadon), 102 (illustrated); Arts Council 1953, 55; Musée Cernuschi 1956; OCS 1960 (Sung), 138

C. 160 Pl. 65b

Pair of bowls with covers. Grey stoneware, covered with olive-green celadon glaze showing some crackle. Decorated outside and on the lid with peonies carved in the paste. Straight foot, with glaze showing whitish where it runs thin. Base glazed inside. The lid has a small knob and is unglazed on the underside, revealing the paste burnt light buff.

The bowls have been broken and repaired with gold lacquer.

Ht. $4\frac{1}{8}''$ Diam. $4\frac{1}{2}''$

Exhib.: OCS 1947 (Celadon), 85; Musée Cernuschi 1956

Cf. One of the pair is reproduced in colour in Madeleine David, 'Céramiques Song', opposite p. 16

C. 257 Pl. 66a

Bowl with everted lip, of grey stoneware decorated inside with a carved floral pattern surrounded by combing, under an olive-green glaze. The square-cut foot and base are unglazed and burnt light reddish-buff.

Ht. $2\frac{1}{8}''$ Diam. $5\frac{1}{2}''$

C. 270 Pl. 66b

Shallow dish of greyish porcellanous stoneware covered with a beautiful soft greyish-green celadon glaze. Decorated in the centre with a carved and combed medallion of peonies, with a band of peony scrolls below the lip. The exterior has a faint spiral line incised under the glaze. The short foot is unglazed on the bottom revealing paste burnt light reddish-buff with a little kiln-sand adhering to it. The deep base is glazed.

Ht. $1\frac{3}{4}''$ Diam. $7\frac{1}{4}''$

C. 379   Pl. 66c

Conical bowl with a straight foot, of grey stoneware burnt greyish-pink where it is exposed. Decorated inside with a moulded design of two babies reclining among large peonies, the design filled in with leaves, surrounded by a narrow scroll-border covered with an olive-brown glaze crackled and stained reddish-brown. Five spur-marks around the centre. The glaze, unevenly applied on the outside over a double incised groove, stops short of the base in an irregular line.

Ht. $2\frac{7}{8}''$ Diam. $7''$
Possibly from Yao-yao

C. 386   Pl. 67a

Round cosmetics box with cover, of light grey stoneware. Inside the box are three small bowls separated by loops. It stands on a thick base with an accretion of kiln-sand. The body is burnt reddish-brown where exposed on the foot and rim. Covered with a crackled celadon glaze olive-green inside, with a bluish-grey tinge outside, discoloured with iron stains round foot and inside base. The lid is decorated with an impressed peony design, and the glaze is similarly greenish inside and bluish-grey outside.

Ht. $1\frac{7}{8}''$ Diam. $5''$
Cf. Pl. 113a in this coll.

C. 284   Pl. 67b

Bowl with everted lip on small foot. Hard porcellanous ware. Decorated with peony scrolls moulded in the paste under an olive-green glaze. In the centre the character Wang[1] (a surname) at the heart of a lotus flower. The shallow foot is unglazed, showing greyish paste with sandy accretions. The base is glazed.

Ht. $2\frac{1}{8}''$ Diam. $4\frac{7}{8}''$

C. 281   Pl. 67c

Conical bowl with everted lip and short foot, of light grey stoneware. Decorated inside with a moulded pattern of peonies, the central blossom having the character Yang[2] (probably a surname) at its heart. Covered with a pale grey-green glaze shading to green in the hollows. The outside is decorated with swiftly executed vertical incisions. The low square-cut foot is unglazed on the bottom, revealing reddish-grey paste. The base is glazed inside.

Ht. $2\frac{7}{8}''$ Diam. $7\frac{7}{8}''$
Possibly from the Yao-yao kilns

[1] See p. 157.   [2] See p. 157.

C. 67   Pl. 68a

Pair of small six-lobed saucers of fine stoneware covered with an olive-green glaze. The glaze stops short of the bottom, which has no foot but has a small hollowed-out ring surrounded with radiating chatter-marks. The exposed paste is burnt reddish buff. Probably originally were placed on stands.

Ht. $\frac{7}{8}''$ Diam. $3\frac{7}{8}''$ and $4''$

Exhib.: OCS 1947 (Celadon), 90

C. 229   Pl. 68b

Conical bowl with everted lip, on small foot, of fine porcellanous stoneware. Decorated inside with four babies playing among lotus plants, moulded in the paste under an olive-green glaze. Shallow foot and base unglazed, showing paste burnt greyish-brown with some accretion of kiln-sand.

Ht. $1\frac{7}{8}''$ Diam. $6\frac{1}{8}''$

Exhib.: Arts Council 1953, 58

C. 244   Pl. 68c

Incense-burner, with globular body, short neck and flaring rim, standing on three short legs. Buff porcellanous body, burnt dark red where exposed on feet, light reddish-brown inside. Covered with a thick irregularly-crazed plum-green glaze.

Ht. $3\frac{1}{8}''$ Diam. $3\frac{7}{8}''$

On the borderline between Northern Celadon and Chün ware; possibly from the Yao-yao kilns in Shensi

Exhib.: Venice 1954, 454 ('The piece has a lighter body than is usually found in Kuan wares and it might be classified among the green Chün')

Publ. Eumo., *Cat.* II, Pl. 18, B. 102 ('?Kuan')

10. Yüeh Ware and Early Celadon

The misty scenery of late autumn appears when the
Yüeh kilns are thrown open:
The thousand peaks have been despoiled of their
bright colour for the decoration of the bowls. . . .
Lu Kuei-meng (IX century), tr. Bushell

Chekiang, the area of the ancient state of Yüeh, is unique in China for the consistence and continuity of her ceramic tradition, and in the refusal of her potters to depart from this tradition during a period of well over a thousand years. By the late T'ang, the Yüeh kilns had perfected a porcelain the jade-like purity of whose glaze was the marvel of the age, the admiration not only of Chinese poets and connoisseurs, but also of the rulers of India and the Near East.

A porcellanous ware, generally imitating bronze shapes, and decorated with impressed designs under a thin olive-green glaze, has been found in late Han tombs not only in and around Hangchow but as far afield as Huang-yen on the seacoast 120 miles to the south-east, and in a tomb dated equivalent to A.D. 99 at Hsin-yang in Honan. The ancestors of these wares, going back to the third century B.C., are believed to have been made in the Shaohsing area, though the kilns have not yet been discovered. However, the kilns at Te-ch'ing north of Hangchow, first visited by Yonaiyama in 1930, are known to have been already active during the Eastern Han period. During the Six Dynasties other kilns grew up to challenge the supremacy of Te-ch'ing, the most famous being the Chiu-yen (Nine Rocks) factory near Shaohsing, first investigated in 1936 and since studied by many scholars, Chinese, Japanese and Western. Chiu-yen continued in production well into the T'ang Dynasty. Early kilns, full details of which have not yet been published, have also been discovered in Shang-yü-hsien and at Ssu-ch'ien-yao; other Six Dynasties kilns have been found at Wang-chia-lou, south of Chiu-yen; at Shang-tung, thirty miles south, and Fu-yang-hsien, thirty miles south-west, of Hangchow; and at Yü-yüan-yao, in Yü-yao-hsien, which was soon to become the main centre for the production of Yüeh wares.

Since 1950, a number of late Han and Six Dynasties tombs have been opened at Nanking, many of which are precisely dated. They were found to contain a wide range of Yüeh wares made in one or other of the Chekiang kilns mentioned above. The early Yüeh pieces in this collection (Pls. 69a & b, 70a & c, 71c) resemble some of the Nanking excavated pieces so closely that we may now date them much more accurately than has hitherto been possible.

Kilns may already have been established at Shang-lin Lake in Yü-yao-hsien in the third century A.D. From humble beginnings they grew to dominate the ceramics industry of Chekiang in the tenth century. Their products received the patronage of the independent princes of the state of Wu-Yüeh from its establishment in 907 until its final surrender to the first Sung Emperor in 978. Thereafter Shang-lin-hu became once more a private factory, but continued to send tribute to the Sung court at Kaifeng at least until 1068. It has been suggested that the term *pi-se* used in admiration of the Yüeh glaze under the late T'ang,

75

MAP III. T'ang and Sung kilns in South-east China

came to mean 'prohibited colour', when the finest of the Shang-lin-hu porcelain was reserved for the exclusive use of the rulers of Wu-Yüeh. The fact that some of the most beautiful examples of *pi-se yao*, decorated with delicately incised decoration under the glaze, were picked up in 1944 by a young Japanese at Yü-wang-miao near Shaohsing, has led to the suggestion that Yü-wang-miao produced wares even finer than those of Shang-lin-hu. So far, however, no kilnsites have been reported there, and recent Chinese authorities are dubious. Yü-wang-miao, for example, is listed as a Chin Dynasty (317–419) kilnsite in *K'ao-ku hsüeh chi-ch'u* (Peking, 1958, p. 239); it is not mentioned, however, among the T'ang and Sung kilnsites listed in *Wen-wu* 1959.5, pp. 70–71. On the other hand, high-quality Yüeh wares with freely-incised designs of the Shang-lin-hu type were certainly made at the recently discovered group of eight Five Dynasties and Sung kilns at Huang-yen. Reports also speak of Yüeh wares having been produced in kilns at Hsi-shan (Western Hill) outside Wenchow (first investigated in 1954), while shards of a Yüeh ware with dark greenish glaze were found in 1953 in Shih-hu-wan-yao, just east of Ching-te-chen in Kiangsi.

In 1957 the Chekiang Provincial Commission for the Preservation of Ancient Monuments conducted a preliminary survey of celadon sites around the shores of Shang-lin-hu, and its two smaller neighbours to the east, Shang-ao-hu and Pai-yang-hu. More than twenty separate kilnsites were identified, with deposits of wasters up to six feet thick. Among the inscribed pieces collected, three were dated 850, 922 and 978. A small fraction of this enormous output was given to export. Fragments of typical Shang-lin-hu ware were found at Brahminabad and in the ruins of Samarra and Fostat, both flourishing in the ninth century; while shards of *pi-se-yao*, together with early *ch'ing-pai* ware, have recently been discovered at Bhamboli, about forty miles south of Karachi, the possible site of the great tenth-century emporium of Debal.

C. 346   Pl. 69a

Funerary bed-pan in the form of a tiger with gaping mouth, and tail twisted over its back in the form of a 'rope-handle'. Light greyish stoneware, covered with a thin greyish-green finely-crackled glaze. Unglazed on base, partly glazed inside.

Ht. 7⅝″ L. 11½″
Yüeh ware, probably from Chiu-yen kilns
III–IV century
Exhib.: Venice 1954, 387
A tomb of the Eastern or Western Chin excavated in Liaoyang contained pottery of Yüeh type, including one of these vessels. The writer of the report notes that there is some doubt as to whether this object was a wine-pot or a bed-pan, but the fact that vessels of this kind have only been found in men's tombs suggests the latter. See *Wen-wu* 1959.7, pp. 60–62

C. 373   Pl. 69b

Sacred cock ewer (*t'ien-chi hu*) of hard fine-grained stoneware with a globular body, short neck and wide flanged mouth-rim. On the shoulder are two small lugs and a short spout terminating in a cock's head with upstanding comb. Covered with a thin olive-green glaze with four brown iron-spots on the rim; iron-spots also on cock's eyes and comb. The glaze runs down unevenly, stopping short of the concave base which is burnt soft reddish-brown. The handle has been broken off and the shoulder and neck repaired.

Ht. 9″ Diam. $7\frac{1}{4}$″

Yüeh ware

IV–VI century

Cf. Ewers of this type found in Eastern Chin tombs in Nanking, *Sekai Tōji Zenshu* VIII, Pl. 18, fig. 175, etc.

The ewer in the form of a cock has been used in Chinese funerary ceremonies for many centuries. In modern times it was still the custom, at least in South China, for the eldest son, after following the coffin to the grave, to sprinkle water from a cock ewer along the road as he returned to the house

C. 116   Pl. 70a

Ovoid jar with wide mouth and everted lip, and two loop-handles on the shoulder. Light buff stoneware body; short slightly splayed and flat base. Cross-hatched round the shoulder under a thin streaky olive-brown glaze which stops short of the base in a wavy line. Glazed inside.

Ht. $4\frac{7}{8}$″ Diam. $5\frac{1}{2}$″

Yüeh ware

VI–VII century

Exhib.: BH 1935, 2484; Manchester 1936, 140; OCS 1949 (T'ang), 102 ('?Pre-T'ang'); Arts Council 1953, 12

C. 374   Pl. 70b

Small ovoid jar with short neck and flat flanged mouth-rim, with lug-handles, and flat base. Grey stoneware, the upper half covered with a dark olive-green glaze.

Ht. 4″ Diam. $3\frac{3}{8}$″

Yüeh ware

VI century

C. 237   Pl. 70c

Ovoid jar of grey stoneware with short straight grooved neck and two small loop-handles. Round the shoulder an impressed diaper pattern. Covered outside with a thin olive-green finely-crackled glaze stopping in an irregular line well short of the concave base. There is no foot-rim and the exposed paste is burnt brick red.

Jars of very similar type have been discovered in a tomb at Nanking dated equivalent to A.D. 237.

Ht. $4\frac{1}{4}$″ Diam. $5\frac{5}{8}$″

Yüeh ware, Chiu-yen type

III–IV centuries

Cf. Nan-ching ch'u-t'u liu-ch'ao ch'ing-tz'u (Celadon excavated from Six Dynasties Tombs at Nanking), fig. 2; Orvar Karlbeck, 'Proto-porcelain and Yüeh Ware',

Trans. OCS 1949–50, Pls. 13 and 14; there are several specimens in the Ingram Coll., Ashmolean Museum, Oxford

S. 26   Pl. 71a

Holder in the form of a kneeling ram, with a socket-hole in its head. Earthenware, covered with a thin unevenly applied crackled olive-green glaze. The eyeballs are picked out with iron-brown spots. There are rough accretions of kiln material on the rump and base.

Ht. 5"   L. $6\frac{1}{8}$"
Yüeh ware, Chiu-yen type
III–V century
Illus.: Gompertz, *Celadon*, Pl. 7A
Cf. Very similar kneeling ram, dated equivalent to A.D. 284, *publ.* in Ch'en Wan-li, *Chung-kuo ch'ing-tz'u shih-lüeh*, Pl. 6

C. 126   Pl. 71b

Holder modelled in the form of a kneeling horned ram with a socket-hole in its head. Light grey buff stoneware, with incipient wing cut in the paste under a thin grey-green glaze. The eyeballs, tips of the horns, ears, nose and tail are picked out with dark brown iron-spots.

Ht. $3\frac{5}{8}$"   L. $4\frac{1}{2}$"
Yüeh ware
Six Dynasties
Cf. Eumo., *Cat.* I, 445–47; Lord Cunliffe coll., Gompertz, *Celadon*, Pl. 7B

C. 171   Pl. 71c

Water dropper (*shui-chu*) in the form of a toad, with head, ears, legs and tail modelled in relief. There is a cruciform motif incised in the paste round the mouth. Porcellanous stoneware covered with a thin grey-green glaze which stops short of the concave base in an uneven line.

Ht. $1\frac{5}{8}$"   Diam. $3\frac{1}{2}$"
Yüeh ware, Chiu-yen type
III–IV century
Exhib.: Arts Council 1953, 11
Cf. Ingram coll., Ashmolean Museum, Oxford, Karlbeck, 'Protoporcelain . . .', *Trans. OCS* 1949–50, Pl. 16f; very similar water-dropper unearthed from tomb dated A.D. 237 in Nanking, *publ. Nan-ching Liu-ch'ao mu ch'u-t'u wen-wu hsüan-chi* (Selected Objects Excavated from Six Dynasties Tombs at Nanking), Shanghai, 1959, Pl. 28

C. 243   Pl. 72a

Ovoid jar of grey porcellanous stoneware carved with petals to suggest a lotus flower. Small mouth and a short foot, surrounded by a raised band. Covered inside and out with a grey glaze having a fine uneven crackle stained brown, and tiny black pitting.

Ht. $4\frac{5}{8}''$ Diam. $5\frac{1}{8}''$
Yüeh ware
IX or X century
Cf. BM *Handbook*, p. 17, fig. 30; ewer with similar body in Ingram coll., Ashmolean
  Museum, Oxford, *publ.* Gompertz, *Celadon*, Pl. 21 ('Five Dynasties or Early
  Sung'); Berlin coll., in Gyllensvärd, *T'ang Gold and Silver*, fig. 39g; very
  similar jars, *Sekai Tōji Zenshu* IX, p. 177, fig. 33

C. 307   Pl. 72b

Jardinière in the shape of a drum with slightly inverted thickened rim and sharply-cut
double ridge round base, supported on four feet with debased masks in relief. Hard grey
stoneware covered with a grey glaze with a faint bluish-green tinge. The base and a large
area inside are unglazed.
  Ht. $1\frac{7}{8}''$ Diam. $5\frac{5}{8}''$
  Yüeh ware
  IX–X century

C. 356   Pl. 72c

Shallow five-lobed dish with slightly everted side, of thin grey stoneware covered with
an olive-green glaze. There is no foot, and the base is slightly concave.
  Ht. $1\frac{3}{8}''$ Diam. $5\frac{1}{2}''$
  Yüeh ware
  T'ang Dynasty

C. 37   Pl. 73

Wine ewer with flattened globular stoneware body and wide slightly flaring neck,
curved spout and strap-handle. On either side a loop-handle faced with a floral ornament
moulded in relief. The body decorated with peonies carved in the paste. Covered inside and
out with an olive-green glaze, crackled on the upper part of the vessel. The low foot and
slightly concave base are unglazed and roughly finished.
  Ht. $6\frac{5}{8}''$ Diam. of body $6\frac{3}{4}''$
  Probably Chekiang celadon
  Sung Dynasty
  Exhib.: BH 1935, 1349 ('Northern Celadon'); Manchester 1936, 179; OCS 1947
    ('Northern Celadon'), 86 (do.); Arts Council 1953, 59 (do.); Venice 1954, 415
    (do.); OCS 1960 (Sung), 155 (under 'Yüeh and allied Wares')
  Publ. Gompertz, *Celadon*, p. 27: 'possibly Li-shui ware, early Sung.' He writes,
    'Koyama believes that the early Sung Li-shui kilns made celadon ware with
    northern or olive-coloured glaze and relief decoration carved underneath.' The
    loop-handles on the shoulder faced with impressed floral motifs are similar in
    technique and style to those on the funerary vase Pl. 75a, which is certainly Yüeh.
    Although not conclusive, this suggests a closer affinity to Chekiang than to the
    north.

Cf. Ewer with rather similar decoration and chicken spout in Eumo., *Cat.* II, Pl. XLVIII, B. 170 ('Northern Celadon')

C. 200   Pl. 74a

Funerary jar with lid, of grey porcellanous stoneware covered with a thick olive-green glaze, shading to greenish-brown at the base. The body of the jar is decorated with carved and striated lotus leaves; the shoulder is divided into three zones by grooves, and covered with a diaper scale pattern. From the shoulder rise five spout-shaped holders for incense sticks or flowers. The glaze runs thickly over the short, slightly splayed foot. The base is glazed and roughly finished, with part of the ring of sand on which it was fired still adhering to it.

The lid is decorated with carved lotus leaves, and terminates in a hollow knob in the shape of a lotus bud. The glaze, where it runs thick in the bottom of the flange, is a dark rich green, full of bubbles.

Ht. $12\frac{1}{2}''$ Diam. $6\frac{1}{4}''$

Yüeh ware

X–XI century

Cf. Similar vase in Hoyt, *Cat.* 230 (called 'Ju ware, celadon', i.e. Northern Celadon); vase in National Museum, Tokyo, *Sekai Tōji Zenshu* X, Colour Pl. 2 ('Yüeh ware'); also *Ibid.*, Pl. 22, Pl. 23 (dated 1080)

C. 305   Pl. 74b

Funerary urn with lid, of greyish ware, covered with a crackled green celadon glaze much decomposed, especially in the lower part, as a result of burial. Five spout-shaped holders for incense-sticks project upward from the shoulder. The body is decorated with two bands of lotus leaves between bands of vertical and slanting flutings incised in the paste under the glaze. The slightly splayed foot is unglazed inside, revealing a paste burnt reddish-brown.

The lid is decorated with incised lotus petals; the knob is in the form of a small vase with fluted body. The flange of the lid sits outside the neck, and the lid, while identical in body and glaze with the vase, may not have belonged to it originally.

Ht. $12\frac{7}{8}''$ Diam. $6\frac{7}{8}''$

Yüeh ware

X–XI century

Cf. Tokyo National Museum, *Sekai Tōji Zenshu* X, Colour Pl. 2; Warren E. Cox coll., Los Angeles 1952, 154; J. C. Thomson coll., OCS 1960 (Sung), 148

C. 278   Pl. 75a

Jar of greyish stoneware with high shoulder, everted neck and flat flanged mouth-rim, covered with a thin greyish glaze which is green where it runs thick on the shoulder. Two small square-cut handles, on either side of the neck, are decorated with peonies modelled in the paste. Beneath them and on either side midway between the handles, a rough floral scroll is freely incised in the paste under the glaze. The glaze stops in an uneven line on the slightly splayed foot. The slightly concave base is partly glazed. The cover is missing.

81

Ht. $13\frac{1}{8}''$ Diam. $6\frac{1}{2}''$
Yüeh ware
X–XI century
Exhib.: Borough of Rawtenstall Art Gallery and Museum, 1936, 1
Cf. Percival David Foundation, 258, dated 1080; Ingram coll., in MEA Oxford, *publ.*
    OCS 1955 (T'ang), 243

C. 380   Pl. 75b

Funerary jar with ovoid six-lobed body, slightly flaring neck and wide flanged mouth, with two small loop-handles on the shoulders. Fine-grained stoneware, covered inside and out with a greyish-green glaze which stops unevenly around the foot. The foot-rim and base are unglazed and burnt reddish-brown.

Ht. $9\frac{7}{8}''$ Diam. $5\frac{5}{8}''$
Yüeh ware
X–XI century
Cf. Vase dated 1080 in Percival David Foundation; several similar specimens, Gompertz, *Celadon*, Pls. 19–22

C. 53   Pl. 76a

Flower bowl with flanged rim standing on a high splayed foot, of light grey stoneware covered with a crackled grey-green glaze. In the centre is a cusped stand in the shape of an inverted lotus, pierced to hold flowers. Round the side are six triple tubular holders made by rolling strips of clay. The exterior is decorated with swiftly-executed vertical incisions. The glaze runs unevenly over the foot which is burnt reddish-brown where exposed. The glaze inside the base is thin and partly decomposed.

Ht. $3\frac{1}{8}''$ Diam. $6\frac{1}{8}''$
Lung-ch'üan celadon
Sung Dynasty, XI century
Cf. Hoyt, *Cat.* 232

C. 201   Pl. 76b

Shallow bowl of lightly-potted light grey hard earthenware, with slightly everted rim, standing on a thin sharply cut foot. Covered with a crackled olive-green celadon glaze which has flaked off in places above and inside the foot. This delicate and unusual piece has been attributed to the Li-shui kilns, but the identification is by no means certain.

Ht. $1\frac{3}{4}''$ Diam. $6\frac{3}{4}''$
Chekiang celadon
XI century

C. 273   Pl. 76c

Lamp, in the form of a flat dish on a small foot, with flanged foliated rim. From the centre rises a hollow square-section support for the wick with chamfered edges, terminating in a little platform in the form of a flower. Whitish porcellanous ware, covered with a greyish-green crackled celadon glaze.

This lamp was purchased with the covered jar, Pl. 88a, and both were shown together as a 'lamp' by S. D. Winkworth at an OCS Specimen meeting and reported in *Trans. OCS* 1930–31, p. 19, but this is quite a different ware, and it seems unlikely that they were originally together.

Ht. $2\frac{1}{4}''$ Diam. $6''$
Lung-ch'üan celadon
Sung Dynasty, XI century

C. 249   Pl. 77a

Funerary vase and cover of greyish porcellanous stoneware, covered with an olive-green celadon glaze. The mouth is splayed and turned in. A tiger modelled in the round encircles the shoulder, stalking amid tongues of flame, and approaching a small frightened dog. Above the tiger on the neck, a sun disk, with the character *jih*[1] (sun) engraved on it, is supported on a cloud. The mouth-rim is unglazed and slightly chipped. The bottom of the short foot is unglazed. The base is partly glazed, and encrusted with the remains of the sagger. The flanged lid has a knob in the form of a bird with head upraised, supported on three ribs ending in scrolls.

Ht. $11''$ Diam. $4\frac{3}{4}''$
Chekiang celadon
About XI century
Cf. Ch'ing-pai vase with iron-brown spots, Hoyt, *Cat.* 384

C. 250   Pl. 77b

Jar with cover, of light grey porcellanous stoneware, with ovoid body, stout neck and wide mouth. The body is decorated with six panels of floral sprays swiftly incised and combed in the paste under an olive-green glaze which stops on the foot. The flat base is unglazed, showing the grey paste with some sandy accretion. The domed lid is decorated with striations under the glaze and has a spout in the form of a hollow jar; partly glazed on the underside.

Ht. $10\frac{7}{8}''$ Diam. $5\frac{1}{4}''$
Yüeh ware
Late X–XI century
Cf. Yüeh-type vase, Ingram coll., in the Ashmolean Museum, Oxford, 'probably X century', Los Angeles 1957, 255; Tokyo National Museum coll., *Sekai Tōji Zenshu* X, Pl. 2, Pl. 22

[1] See p. 157.

11. Kuan *Ware and Celadon, Sung and Later*

Taken together with the Yüeh wares, the ninety specimens in this collection present almost the full range of celadon types, extending in date from the first centuries A.D. up to the eighteenth century, and in quality from the finest court wares of the Southern Sung to the coarse but vigorously-potted export stoneware of South China. Most of the pieces were made in Chekiang, the home of the celadons. Two are certainly Hangchow *kuan* of classic type, a half dozen or so Lung-ch'üan ware of such exquisite quality that they should surely rank as palace pieces.

Chinese connoisseurship traditionally draws a clear distinction between *kuan* wares made at the Hangchow kilns for the Southern Sung court on the one hand, and all other Chekiang celadons, whatever their quality, on the other. But the question of precisely what was and was not *kuan* under the Southern Sung is now, after the lapse of eight hundred years, hardly any nearer solution than the problem of 'northern *kuan*'.

The Southern Sung work *T'an-chai pi-heng* by Yeh Chih states that after the move to the south a bureau was set up by Shao Ch'eng-chang, Supervisor of Parks, called Shao's Office, to duplicate utensils which had been preserved from the former capital. These presumably included all kinds of objects for courtly use, and not only porcelain; for after its long wanderings, the Southern Sung court made every effort to recapture the glories of its former life in Kaifeng. Shao, the *T'an-chai pi-heng* continues, 'set up kilns at the Surveyor's Office (*Hsiu-nei Ssu*), where he made a celadon which was called *Nei-yao* (Palace ware). Its pure body of exceptional fineness and delicacy, its clear and lustrous glaze, have caused it to be prized ever since. Later another ware was made below the Suburban Altar (*Chiao-t'an*), quite different from the old ware.' Great efforts have been made to locate the site of the Hsiu-nei Ssu kilns, but thirty years' search has failed to reveal them. The area was extensively built over in the twelfth century, and though a good deal of ceramic material has been found on the site, including the fine uncrackled, light-bodied ware mentioned in the *T'an-chai pi-heng*, expert opinion is divided as to whether it points to an actual kilnsite or merely to normal occupation. Recent Chinese writers on the subject remain sceptical, and the Hsiu-nei Ssu is not among the Chekiang kilnsites, known or merely recorded, that are listed in an inventory of T'ang and Sung kilns published in *Wen-wu* 1959.3. If indeed there were kilns at the Hsiu-nei Ssu, their belching furnaces must have proved a great nuisance to occupants of the palace, especially when the wind was in the west, and it would be easy to understand why a new site further away was so soon found for them. A few beautiful celadons with a white body and exquisite blue uncrackled glaze have been identified by Japanese experts as Hsiu-nei Ssu ware; but this attribution is not universally accepted.

This collection includes two examples of the *kuan* ware made at the official kilns set up below the Chiao-t'an, at the southern end of the low range of hills running south from the modern city of Hangchow, well away from the Sung Palace. The site has been a place of pilgrimage to ceramic enthusiasts ever since its rediscovery by Jen Chou in 1929. The thin grey body of the Chiao-t'an ware has generally oxidized black in the reducing atmosphere of the kiln, and is covered with a thick, lustrous, crackled glaze applied in several coats, and varying in colour between greyish-blue (Pl. 78a) and blue-green (Pl. 78b). The soft luminosity of this most beautiful of all Southern Sung glazes is due to its rough surface and to the presence of large bubbles, which scatter and diffuse the light in its depths, and to a crackle handled with a restraint perfectly in keeping with the subtlety of the glaze.

There are in the collection several notable examples of celadon of the very finest quality which, because they lack the black body, would be rejected by purists as true *kuan* and consigned to Lung-chü'an, or cautiously labelled 'Hangchow celadon of *kuan* type'. These include the conical bowl (Colour Pl. D) which is, understandably, Sir Alan Barlow's favourite piece; the pair of octagonal bottles (Pl. 82a), and the three kinuta-shaped vases (Pls. 80a and 81b). However, it is known that the Chiao-t'an kilns also produced a light-bodied, uncrackled ware, and it seems possible that the lovely bottle (Pl. 81b) might have been made there.

The position regarding the source, or sources, of Hangchow *kuan* ware was further complicated by the discovery at Lung-ch'üan of a kiln-waster (now in the Metropolitan Museum in New York), consisting of two bowls fused together, one of which had a light body and uncrackled glaze, the other being dark-bodied under a crackled glaze. There is no need, therefore, to assume that all so-called *kuan* wares were made in the imperial kilns at Hangchow, or that they were identical in body and glaze. There must have been some variety in the body and glaze-colour of wares passed for the palace at the beginning, and it seems likely that if a rigid uniformity was prescribed at all, it was maintained only in theory. Moreover, it seems very probable that standards were progressively relaxed, and that varieties of the original wares were accepted for the imperial table in the thirteenth century which would have been rejected in the twelfth.

Ch'en Wan-li, in his study of celadons *Chung-kuo Ch'ing-tz'u Shih-lüeh* lists thirty-two main kiln centres in the Lung-ch'üan district. He identifies six, of which the chief was Ta-yao, as being active from the Sung to the Ming; six as operating in the Sung Dynasty only; three during both Yüan and Ming; ten during the Ming only; one through Ming and Ch'ing; the remainder from Ch'ing to the present day. This shows that with the removal of the capital to Peking under the Yüan, and the rise of the gigantic factory at Ching-te-chen, the output of Lung-ch'üan did not decrease. On the contrary, although there was some decline in quality, production was maintained at a high level to meet local needs and the ever-growing demands of the export trade. Kilns were also set up during the Ming Dynasty at Ch'u-chou near Li-shui; but it would be quite wrong to label all Ming and later Chekiang celadons as Ch'u-chou ware, though this is often done.

Little work has yet been done towards dating the celadons within the Southern Sung period. Koyama has suggested that the elaborate funerary jars made in pairs and adorned with tigers and dragons, and the jars with five spouts projecting up from the shoulder, are survivals of earlier types, and that some of them were produced before the end of Northern Sung. While this seems likely in the case of the grave jar (Pl. 74a), it could hardly apply to pieces of the superb quality of Pls. 86a and 87, which we may confidently assign to the twelfth century.

KUAN WARE AND CELADON, SUNG AND LATER

In their quiet way, the celadons in this collection present an epitome of changing Chinese taste from the Sung Dynasty to the eighteenth century. The Lung-ch'üan wares rely for their beauty on the simple dignity of their shape, and on a glaze colour of exquisite subtlety — blue-green, tempered by grey — which seems a perfect expression of the dreamy refinement of aristocratic life in Hangchow during the long period of calm before the catastrophic descent of the Mongols. The change seems to have come in the thirteenth and fourteenth centuries. Shapes multiply and become more self-conscious and elaborate; moulded or incised decoration is borrowed from other ceramic families, notably from blue and white (Pls. 89a, 95b, 98a and 99a); while the soft blue-grey is drained out of the glaze leaving it a cold transparent sea-green, which is seldom if ever beautiful. The most interesting among the later celadons are the least sophisticated, notably the rougher popular and export wares. Among the former we find inscribed pieces of unusual interest (Pls. 95c, 96c and 97c), among the latter the huge dishes made specially for export to the Near East and South-East Asia, where they have been treasured for centuries as family heirlooms. A Japanese archaeologist has reported that large celadon dishes of the type of Pls. 102a, 102b and 103a were used by coastal tribes in New Guinea, who kept them buried in the sand, digging them up only to use in feasts and celebrations. Many were made in kilns now being properly investigated for the first time, in Fukien and Kwangtung. Owing to the persistence of old ceramic traditions in these provincial centres, their products are difficult to date with any precision.

Ko Ware

The so-called *ko* ware, with its close, artificially darkened crackle, is a variety of celadon which appealed much to Chinese antiquarian taste. The legend of the elder (*ko*) of the Chang brothers who made this ware at Lung-ch'üan is now little regarded, but *ko* is a convenient name for a sophisticated class of wares closer in spirit, if not in body, to Chiao-t'an *kuan* than to the rest of the Lung-ch'üan output, and it is significant that Ch'en Wan-li and other recent Chinese writers retain it. There is reason to think that it may also have been made at the Hangchow imperial kilns. The lovely brush-washer (Pl. 79a) and the bowl (Pl. 91a) are both Sung specimens, probably of the late twelfth or thirteenth century; the remaining three show how closely the original ware was copied at Ching-te-chen in the eighteenth century.

C. 13   Colour Pl. D

Conical bowl on small shallow foot. Stoneware, burnt red on exposed foot-rim. Covered with a sea-green glaze having a wide crack stained brown and a finer unstained secondary crackle. Lip mounted in copper.

Ht. $2\frac{1}{8}''$ Diam. $6''$
Kuan ware
Southern Sung Dynasty
Exhib.: BH 1935, 884 ('Kuan'); Manchester 1936, 176; OCS 1952 (Ju, Kuan), 98 ('Chekiang celadon')

86

D. Conical bowl. Stoneware, covered with crackled celadon glaze. Southern *kuan* ware. Diam. 6″. Southern Sung Dynasty. (C.13, page 86)

Publ. Gompertz, *Celadon*, Pl. 56A ('S. Kuan')
Cf. A large deeper bowl of this type, its lobed lip bound in gold, reproduced in colour
   as Pl. 14, *Chinese Ceramics, 100 Masterpieces* (Tokyo, 1960) ('Kuan')

C. 236   Pl. 78a

Vase, with depressed globular body, broad neck and flattened cup-shaped lip, standing on
high, thin and slightly splayed foot. Porcellanous stoneware burnt reddish-black on foot-
rim; covered with a warm grey-blue crackled glaze.
   Said to have been found in a grave in Feng-hsiang-hsien, north of Hangchow.
      Ht. $5\frac{1}{4}''$ Diam. $3\frac{3}{8}''$
      Hangchow *kuan* ware
      Southern Sung Dynasty
      Exhib.: Dartington Hall 1949, 88; OCS 1952 (Ju and Kuan), 35; Musée Cernuschi 1956
      Publ. Gompertz, Pl. 57A; Gray, *Early Chinese Pottery and Porcelain*, Pl. 86
      Cf. Venice 1954, 435; a group of similar pieces excavated from the Hangchow altar
         site is illustrated in *Sekai Tōji Zenshu* X, p. 191, fig. 28

C. 215   Pl. 78b

Bowl, with flaring lip and small, short foot; roughly modelled lotus petals round the outside. Hard stoneware burnt dark reddish-brown on lip and exposed foot-rim. Covered with
a dark bluish-green unevenly-crackled glaze.
      Ht. $2''$ Diam. $5\frac{1}{2}''$
      Kuan ware
      Southern Sung Dynasty

C. 12   Pl. 79a

Brush-washer with concave base, straight side and foliated lip. Dark stoneware, covered
with thick well controlled grey glaze with delicate but clearly defined crackle. Five spur-
marks on the base.
      Ht. $1\frac{3}{8}''$ Diam. $4\frac{5}{8}''$
      Ko ware
      Sung Dynasty
      Exhib.: OCS 1952 (Ju and Kuan), 72 ('XIII century')
      Cf. Garner coll., OCS 1952 (Ju and Kuan), 67; Venice 1954, 460. This type with
         spur-marks is discussed by Garner in 'Early Chinese Crackled Porcelain', *Trans.
         OCS* 1960 (*Cat.* of Sung Exhib.) p. 25; he suggests that they are late Sung or
         Yüan. There are many pieces of this type in the Palace Museum coll. and in the
         Percival David Foundation

C. 220   Pl. 79b

Flat dish of dark stoneware with hollow base, standing on short elegantly cut foot.
Covered with a thick unctuous grey glaze having an even, strongly marked primary crackle
stained black, and a yellowish-brown secondary crackle.

Ht. 1″ Diam. $6\frac{1}{4}$″
Ching-te-chen *ko* type celadon
XVIII century

C. 181   Pl. 79c

Flat dish with everted and foliated side standing on a short base, the foot-rim unglazed. Dark brown stoneware, covered with a heavily-crackled light greyish glaze, showing slight decomposition.

Ht. $1\frac{3}{4}$″ Diam. $7\frac{3}{8}$″
Chekiang celadon of *ko* type
Date uncertain, possibly Ming Dynasty

C. 104   Pl. 79d

Flat six-lobed saucer dish on shallow straight-cut foot. Dark stoneware covered with rather glassy grey glaze which is burnt brown at lip and around base. Wide uneven crackle partly stained black. Seven spur-marks on underside.

Ht. 1″ Diam. $6\frac{3}{8}$″
Ko type, Ching-te-chen ware
XVIII century
Publ. BH 1935, *Cat.* 878 ('Sung Ko ware')
Cf. Dish in Percival David Foundation with Ch'ien-lung inscription

C. 74   Pl. 80a

Pair of *kinuta* ('mallet')-shaped vases, with barrel-shaped body, straight neck and broad rim. Handles with phoenix-heads on either side of the neck. Light grey porcellanous stoneware, covered with a fine-crackled bluish-green glaze. The glaze stops just short of the foot which is burnt light buff. Glazed inside the slightly concave base.

Ht. $6\frac{5}{8}$″ Diam. $2\frac{7}{8}$″
Lung-ch'üan celadon
Sung Dynasty
Exhib.: OCS 1947 (Celadon), 42; Venice 1954, 423

C. 73   Pl. 80b

Deep bowl of porcellanous stoneware, on small foot, decorated outside with carved lotus petals, under green celadon glaze. Body burnt brown on exposed foot-rim. Glazed inside base.

Ht. $2\frac{3}{4}$″ Diam. $5\frac{7}{8}$″
Lung-ch'üan celadon
Sung Dynasty, XII–XIII century
Exhib.: OCS 1947 (Celadon), 35

C. 77   Pl. 81a

Jar with lid, of very thinly-potted translucent grey porcelain covered with a thick unctuous oyster-grey glaze. The base is crackled, the thin unglazed foot-rim misshapen in the firing. The slightly domed lid has a small flat knob and is unglazed on the underside of the flange, revealing the paste burnt light buff; it has been broken in half, and repaired at the lip.

Evidently a kiln-waster, but of lovely quality.

Ht. (total) $2\frac{3}{4}''$ Diam. $3\frac{1}{2}''$

Lung-ch'üan celadon

Sung Dynasty, XII century

Publ. Hetherington, *Early Ceramic Wares*, p. 104 and Pl. 26, F. 2 ('Lung-ch'üan'); in colour, Hobson, *Chinese Art* (1927) Pl. XIX

C. 36   Pl. 81b

Kinuta ('mallet')-shaped vase, with cylindrical body, sloping shoulder, straight neck and broad rim; with handles in the shape of fishes on either side of the neck. Light grey stoneware covered inside and out with a thick unctuous light blue-green glaze known as *fen-ch'ing* (powder blue-green). The bottom of the foot is unglazed and burnt reddish-brown. Glazed inside the base. This must be one of the most perfect specimens in existence.

Ht. $6\frac{5}{8}''$ Diam. $2\frac{7}{8}''$

Lung-ch'üan celadon

Sung Dynasty

Exhib.: BH 1935, 1310; Manchester 1936, 222; OCS 1947 (Celadon), 11; Arts Council 1953, 63

Cf. Vase with flanged mouth (*p'an-k'ou-p'ing*) in Chinese Government coll., BH 1935, 1375

C. 71   Pl. 81c

Bulb-bowl or brush-washer of light grey porcellanous ware, on three mask feet, covered with a fine green celadon glaze. The drum-shaped bowl is decorated around rim and above feet with bands of round bosses in relief. The bottom of the bowl has an unglazed 'foot-rim'. Glazed inside the base.

Ht. $3\frac{1}{4}''$ Diam. $6\frac{3}{8}''$

Lung-ch'üan celadon

Sung Dynasty

Exhib.: OCS 1947 (Celadon), 26

Cf. Percival David Foundation, BH 1935, 1314

C. 75   Pl. 82a

Pair of octagonal bottles (*pa-leng-p'ing*) with straight slightly tapering neck and flat rim, standing on a slightly splayed foot pierced on opposite sides. Light grey porcellanous stoneware, covered inside and out with a thick, unctuous widely-crackled green celadon glaze. The bottom of the foot-rim is unglazed and burnt buff. Glazed inside the base.

Ht. $8\frac{1}{8}''$ Diam. $5\frac{3}{8}''$

Lung-ch'üan celadon

Sung Dynasty

Exhib.: BH 1935, 1335; OCS 1947 (Celadon), 16; OCS 1952 (Ju and Kuan), 89; Arts Council 1953, 60; OCS 1960 (Sung), 168

Publ. Gray, *ECPP* Colour Pl. D ('Lung-ch'üan celadon'); Mayuyama, *Chinese Ceramics in the West*, Pl. 53 ('South Sung, *Kuan* yao'); Gompertz, *Celadon*, p. 46 and Pl. 62 'Chekiang celadon of *Kuan* type'

C. 100   Pl. 82b

Pair of vessels called *hsien-wen p'ing* ('string-lined vases'), with depressed globular slightly ribbed body and tapering tubular neck, the mouth everted and turned in at the lip. Light grey stoneware covered with a fine blue-grey uncrackled celadon glaze, of exceptionally beautiful colour, close to that of Ju-yao. Rather high straight foot, unglazed and burnt reddish-brown on the bottom of the foot-rim. Glazed inside the flat base.

Ht. $6\frac{3}{4}''$ Diam. $4''$
Lung-ch'üan celadon
Sung Dynasty, XII century
Exhib.: OCS 1952 (Ju and Kuan), 92; Arts Council 1953, 69; Musée Cernuschi 1956
Publ. Madeleine David, 'Céramiques Song', fig. 5
Cf. David coll., *Cat.* Pl. XLI; BH 1935, 1305; Eumo., *Cat.* II, Pl. XXX, B. 114

C. 137   Pl. 82c

Bowl of buff stoneware, covered with a crackled greyish-blue/green celadon glaze, slightly decomposed through burial. Sharply cut foot burnt reddish on exposed rim. Glazed inside base.

Ht. $2\frac{5}{8}''$ Diam. $6\frac{3}{8}''$
Lung-ch'üan celadon
Sung Dynasty

C. 170   Pl. 83a

'Arrow jar' in the form of a bottle with globular body and straight neck with two tubular handles. Light greyish porcelain, covered inside and out with fine thick green celadon glaze. High foot glazed inside base. The exposed foot-rim is burnt light reddish-brown.

Ht. $4''$ Diam. $3''$
Lung-ch'üan celadon
Sung Dynasty
Exhib.: OCS 1947 (Celadon), 9; Arts Council 1953, 65

C. 125   Pl. 83b

Bowl of greyish porcelain on small foot with everted rim. Lotus petals carved outside under a green widely-crackled celadon glaze. Body burnt reddish where exposed on foot-rim. Some decomposition in centre and on base. Lip repaired with gold lacquer.

Ht. $1\frac{5}{8}''$ Diam. $3\frac{7}{8}''$
Lung-ch'üan celadon
Sung Dynasty

C. 70   Pl. 83c

Conical bowl on small foot. Greyish-white porcelain, covered with a fine creamy greyish-green glaze. The body burnt brown where exposed on the foot-rim.

Ht. $1\frac{7}{8}''$ Diam. $5''$
Lung-ch'üan celadon
Sung Dynasty
Cf. Eumo., *Cat.* II, B. 124

C. 182   Pl. 84a

Bowl of greyish-white porcelain, decorated outside with lotus petals carved under a pale bluish-grey widely-crackled celadon glaze. The bottom of the small foot is unglazed and the exposed paste burnt brown. Glazed inside the base.

Ht. $2\frac{7}{8}''$ Diam. $6\frac{5}{8}''$
Lung-ch'üan celadon
Sung Dynasty
Exhib.: OCS 1947 (Celadon), 22; Arts Council 1953, 62
Cf. Hoyt, *Cat.* 218; BH 1935, 44

C. 187   Pl. 84b

Small bowl of fine-grained stoneware, with flattened everted rim, decorated inside with two fishes in relief, the outside fluted suggesting lotus petals. Covered with a finely-crackled crystalline yellowish-brown glaze, the unusual colour being due to its having been fired in an oxidizing atmosphere. Foot-rim sharply cut and unglazed on the bottom. Glazed inside the base.

Ht. $1\frac{5}{8}''$ Diam. $5\frac{1}{4}''$
Lung-ch'üan celadon
Sung Dynasty
Exhib.: Dartington Hall 1949, 84; OCS 1947 (Celadon), 56

C. 210   Pl. 84c

Small bowl of sturdily-potted porcellanous ware with moulded lotus petals on the outside, covered with a grey-green crackled celadon glaze. The bottom of the straight foot is unglazed and burnt reddish-buff. Glazed inside the base.

Ht. $1\frac{7}{8}''$ Diam. $3\frac{1}{2}''$
Lung-ch'üan celadon
Sung Dynasty

C. 78   Pl. 85a

Jar with cover, of thin whitish porcellanous ware burnt light brown where it is exposed on rim and bottom of foot of jar. The side decorated with lotus petals carved in the paste under a bluish-green celadon glaze. Glazed inside the base. The slightly domed lid is adorned with lotus petals surrounding a tiny knob. The underside of the flange is unglazed, burnt light reddish-brown with some discoloration.

Ht. $2\frac{5}{8}''$ Diam. $3\frac{3}{4}''$
Lung-ch'üan celadon
Sung Dynasty, XII century
Exhib.: Arts Council 1953, 66
Cf. Very similar covered bowl in BM, Gray, *Early Chinese Pottery and Porcelain*, Pl. 89

C. 38 Pl. 85b

Potiche and cover of sturdily-potted light greyish porcellanous ware; the body decorated with incised lines round the middle, covered with a thick blue-green celadon glaze with three brown ferruginous spots. The mouth-rim and chamfered foot are unglazed and burnt light brown; glazed inside the base. The flat lid has a foliate edge and four iron-spots; the underside of the flange is unglazed.

Ht. $2\frac{5}{8}''$ Diam. $3''$
Lung-ch'üan *tobi-seiji* (buckwheat celadon)
Sung Dynasty
Exhib.: OCS 1947 (Celadon), 63; Arts Council 1953, 67
Cf. Trans. OCS 1922–23, Pl. 2 (2)

C. 136 Pl. 85c

Deep bowl of greyish-white porcellanous ware, decorated outside with carved lotus petals, under a greenish-grey crackled celadon glaze. The body burnt brown where exposed on foot. Glazed inside base.

Ht. $2\frac{5}{8}''$ Diam. $5\frac{1}{8}''$
Lung-ch'üan celadon
Sung Dynasty

C. 186 Pl. 85d

Conical bowl on small foot, of fine-grained greyish porcelain, burnt light reddish-brown where exposed on the foot-rim. Covered with a fine greenish celadon glaze. Round the outside above the foot are a series of vertical striations incised in the paste under the glaze.

Ht. $2''$ Diam. $5\frac{7}{8}''$
Lung-ch'üan celadon
Sung Dynasty
Exhib.: OCS 1947 (Celadon), 76; Venice 1954, 424

C. 280 Pl. 86a

Funerary jar of greyish porcelain, covered outside and part of interior with a rich creamy grey-green celadon glaze, shading to grey and lightly-crackled on the lower half of the body. Around the shoulder is applied a vigorously modelled four-clawed dragon chasing a flaming pearl. Straight foot unglazed on bottom of foot-rim. Glazed inside base. The lip is chipped, and appears to have been slightly ground down. The slightly domed lid has a wide flange and a knob in the form of a bird. The lid is unglazed on the underside.

Ht. $9\frac{3}{4}''$ Diam. $4\frac{1}{2}''$

Lung-ch'üan celadon
Sung Dynasty, XII century
Cf. Very similar jar in Eumo., *Cat.* II, Pl. XXIX, B. 111

C. 335   Pl. 86b

Feeding-bowl for a bird-cage; conical, with pointed base, inverted rim and small ring-handle at one side. Made in two halves of greyish porcellanous stoneware, and covered with a fine, even grey-green *kinuta*-type celadon glaze.

Ht. $1\frac{7}{8}''$ Diam. $2\frac{3}{8}''$
Lung-ch'üan celadon, very close to Korean Koryŏ ware
Sung Dynasty
Exhib.: OCS 1952 (Ju and Kuan), 93

C. 315   Pl. 86c

Potiche and cover of sturdily-potted light greyish porcellanous ware, decorated with thick green celadon glaze, with brown ferruginous spots. The rim, foot and base of the jar and the underside of the lid are unglazed and burnt reddish-brown.

Ht. $2\frac{1}{2}''$ Diam. $3\frac{1}{8}''$
Lung-ch'üan *tobi-seiji* (buckwheat celadon)
Sung Dynasty
Cf. Schiller coll., Bristol City Art Gallery, Venice 1954, 426 ('Sung or Yüan')

C. 357   Pl. 87

Funerary jar of greyish porcelain with short tubular neck, covered inside and out with a fine grey-green crackled celadon glaze. A four-clawed dragon modelled in high relief encircles the shoulder, confronting a pearl and a bird, also in appliqué. The base is glazed, the foot-rim unglazed and burnt reddish-brown. The shallow domed lid has a knob in the form of a sitting dog with head and tail upraised.

Ht. $10\frac{1}{8}''$ Diam. $5''$
Lung-ch'üan celadon
Sung Dynasty, XII century
Cf. Pair of similar jars in Percival David Foundation, Nos. 204a & b

C. 272   Pl. 88a

Jar and cover of sturdily-potted light grey porcellanous ware, covered with a pale blue-green celadon glaze. The base of the jar is separately potted and luted in, perhaps as a replacement for a fault in the original firing. The lid is slightly foliated, suggesting a lotus leaf, the paste burnt pinkish on the underside where it is not glazed.

This jar is published with the lamp (Pl. 76c) inside it, in *Trans. OCS* 1930–31.

Ht. $6\frac{1}{2}''$ Diam. $7\frac{1}{4}''$
Lung-ch'üan celadon
Sung Dynasty
Exhib.: Arts Council 1953, 64 (with lamp)

C. 267   Pl. 88b

Funerary vase with high shoulder, small neck and flanged mouth, with five spout-shaped holders for incense rising from the shoulder. Greyish porcelain. Body fluted, suggesting lotus petals. Covered with a thick greenish celadon glaze showing blue where it runs thick. Roughly cut foot-rim unglazed. Glazed inside base. The unusual shape is derived from that of the larger Yüeh ware funerary vases of which there are two in this collection.

> Ht. $4\frac{3}{4}''$ Diam. $5\frac{1}{4}''$
> Lung-ch'üan celadon
> Sung Dynasty, XII century

C. 44   Pl. 89a

Baluster vase with wide neck and flaring lip, of stoutly-potted porcellanous ware, burnt reddish-brown where it is exposed on the short sharply chamfered foot. The neck is grooved, the body is decorated with carved peonies above a band of lotus petals, under a greenish-grey celadon glaze shading to olive towards the foot. Glazed inside the base.

> Ht. $11\frac{5}{8}''$ Diam. $5\frac{1}{2}''$
> Lung-ch'üan celadon
> Probably XIII–XIV century
> *Cf.* A similar vase in the Ardebil collection attributed by John Pope to the XIV–XV
>   century, *publ. Chinese Porcelains from the Ardebil Shrine*, Pl. 129, 29. 648

C. 56   Pl. 89b

Jar (*mei-p'ing*), with high shoulder and small mouth, of light greyish porcellanous ware burnt reddish-brown where exposed. The body decorated with horizontal ribbing under a fine green celadon glaze. Short foot sharply cut and unglazed. Glaze inside the base partly pitted.

> Ht. $7\frac{3}{4}''$ Diam. $4\frac{3}{4}''$
> Lung-ch'üan celadon
> Sung Dynasty, late XII–XIII century
> *Exhib.:* Arts Council 1953, 68

C. 133   Pl. 89c

Narcissus bowl (*shui-hsien p'en*) in the shape of a drum, decorated with two bands of studs and three cloud-scroll feet; the vessel actually stands on a short circular foot, unglazed on the foot-rim. Stoneware, burnt red where exposed, and covered with a thick much-pitted light greyish glaze having a dark grey primary and light reddish secondary crackle. Five spur-marks inside bottom. Broken and repaired.

> Ht. $2\frac{7}{8}''$ Diam. $6\frac{3}{8}''$
> Lung-ch'üan imitation of Chiao-t'an *kuan* ware
> XIII–XIV century
> *Exhib.:* OCS 1952 (Ju and Kuan), 87 ('Sung Kuan ware')
> *Cf.* David coll., *Cat.* Pl. 33

C. 52   Pl. 90a

Shallow flat dish of porcellanous stoneware, with flanged rim, decorated with two dragons in relief under a pale green celadon glaze. Foot unglazed and burnt brown; glazed inside base. Rim chipped in two places and repaired with gold lacquer.

Ht. $1\frac{1}{4}''$ Diam. $6\frac{5}{8}''$
Lung-ch'üan celadon
XIII–XIV century
Cf. Lung-ch'üan dish in private coll., London, Venice 1954, 430

C. 327   Pl. 90b

Vase with ovoid body, straight neck and slightly everted lip. On the neck, ring handles with animal masks and pendant rings. Heavily-potted stoneware made in two parts luted together, the joint marked by a rib round the body. Covered inside and out with a matt green glaze which stops at the chamfered foot. Glazed inside the base.

Ht. $7\frac{1}{8}''$ Diam. $3\frac{1}{2}''$
Lung-ch'üan celadon
XIII–XIV century
Exhib.: Arts Council 1953, 68 ('Sung or Yüan Dynasty')

C. 179   Pl. 90c

Pair of ovoid jars with flat covers having knobs in the form of elephants. Grey stoneware burnt red where exposed on rim and bottom of foot-rim and on underside of flange of cover. Covered with a finely-crackled grey-green celadon glaze. The hollow base is glazed.

Ht. $5\frac{1}{2}''$ and $5\frac{1}{8}''$ Diam. $3\frac{1}{2}''$ and $3\frac{3}{4}''$
Chekiang celadon
Sung Dynasty XII–XIII century

C. 124   Pl. 91a

Bowl with slightly everted lip, standing on small sharply finished foot. Body burnt brown where exposed on foot-rim. Covered with a greenish-grey *kuan*-type glaze with clearly defined crackle on the outside; crackle inside less clearly marked except where there is brown staining in the bottom.

Ht. $2\frac{1}{4}''$ Diam. $4\frac{3}{4}''$
Chekiang celadon
Sung Dynasty
Exhib.: OCS 1952 (Ju and Kuan), 85

C. 232   Pl. 91b

Small jar with cover. Grey porcellanous ware, covered with a greyish-olive crackled celadon glaze. The jar is moulded on the outside with lotus petals. The rim and bottom of foot arc unglazed, but it is glazed inside the base. The slightly domed cover also has lotus petals moulded round a barely perceptible boss; the underside of the flange is unglazed and burnt reddish-buff. Said to have been found at Wen-chou.

Ht. $2\frac{3}{4}''$ Diam. $3\frac{1}{2}''$
Chekiang celadon
Sung Dynasty, XII century

C. 173   Pl. 91c

Small bowl on high foot, the side ribbed to suggest lotus leaves. Greyish porcellanous ware burnt red on the exposed foot-rim. Covered with a grey-green celadon type glaze, full of bubbles and very dark green where thick.

Ht. $1\frac{3}{4}''$ Diam. $3\frac{1}{8}''$
Chekiang celadon
Sung Dynasty

C. 197   Pl. 91d

Bowl with slightly everted lip, on a small foot. Grey stoneware covered, except for the bottom of the foot-rim, with a finely-crackled golden-brown glaze. Lotus petals carved on the outside under the glaze.

Ht. $2\frac{1}{2}''$ Diam. $5\frac{3}{4}''$
Chekiang celadon
Sung Dynasty, XII century

C. 254   Pl. 92a

Bowl and stand, of greyish porcellanous stoneware, covered with a crackled green celadon glaze. The bowl is decorated inside with a spray of prunus incised in the paste under the glaze. The bottom of the foot-rim is burnt reddish-brown where it is exposed. The stand is in the form of a potiche with a broad flange upturned at the edge. There is an unglazed band round the base and round the inside of the rim.

Bowl Ht. $1\frac{1}{2}''$ Diam. $4\frac{1}{4}''$
Stand Ht. $1\frac{3}{4}''$ Diam. $4\frac{1}{2}''$
Chekiang celadon
XIII–XIV century
Cf. below, C. 317 (Pl. 94b) in this coll., similar bowl without the stand

C. 35   Pl. 92b

Vase in the shape of a *ting* tripod, with two loop-handles and a hole through centre of base, standing on three hollow legs. Stoutly-potted porcellanous ware, covered with a thick and unctuous pale green celadon glaze which is pitted here and there inside the bowl. Lower protruding rim of hole and underside of feet are unglazed, showing body burnt reddish-brown.

Ht. $5\frac{1}{2}''$ Diam. $5''$
Chekiang celadon
Sung Dynasty
Exhib.: OCS 1947 (Celadon), 65

C. 266   Pl. 92c

Jar with wide neck and everted and turned-in rim, of greyish porcelain covered inside and out with thick egg-shell-grey celadon-type glaze. The bottom of the foot is unglazed and burnt light reddish-buff. Glazed inside the base. Its unusual colour suggests that this is probably a kiln-waster.

Ht. $7\frac{3}{4}''$ Diam. $5''$
Chekiang celadon
Sung Dynasty, XII century

C. 113   Pl. 92d

Small bowl of thickly-potted grey stoneware with thickened rim, standing on a small roughly finished rounded foot. Covered with a pale greyish-green unevenly applied celadon glaze, which is milky-white where it runs thick. Where the body is exposed it is burnt brown.

Ht. $1\frac{7}{8}''$ Diam. $4\frac{1}{4}''$
Chekiang celadon
Sung Dynasty, probably XI century

C. 375   Pl. 93a

Bowl on small foot, of greyish porcellanous ware, decorated inside with lotus flowers freely incised in the paste under a matt olive-green celadon glaze. The exterior decorated with roughly sketched lotus leaves; round the rim triple incised lines, the middle line broken by zig-zags at intervals. The body is burnt rich reddish where it is exposed on the foot. The base is glazed inside.

Ht. $3\frac{1}{8}''$ Diam. $7\frac{7}{8}''$
Chekiang celadon
XIII–XIV century

C. 275   Pl. 93b

Bowl with everted foliate lip in the form of a lotus leaf, standing on a small foot. Light greyish porcelain covered with a thick transparent crackled grey-green celadon glaze. A small tortoise is modelled in relief in the centre, while the veins of the leaf are indicated by incision in the paste under the glaze. The edge of the lip is brownish where the glaze is thin. The exterior is plain but for a suggestion of concentric rings near the foot. The foot-rim is unglazed, revealing the paste burnt reddish-brown. Glazed inside the base.

Ht. $2''$ Diam. $4\frac{1}{2}''$
Chekiang celadon
Sung Dynasty

C. 295   Pl. 93c

Dish of greyish porcellanous stoneware, decorated with lotus petals freely moulded on the outside under a soft olive-grey celadon glaze. Foot-rim unglazed and slightly chipped. Glazed inside base.

Ht. $2\frac{1}{4}''$ Diam. $8\frac{1}{2}''$
Chekiang celadon
Sung Dynasty

C. 209   Pl. 94a

Pear-shaped bottle with slender neck and everted mouth-rim standing on a slightly splayed foot. Two tubular handles are placed high on the neck. Porcellanous stoneware made in two sections luted together at the shoulder. The body is decorated with peony scrolls cut in the paste under a pale green celadon glaze. The unglazed foot-rim is burnt buff; the base is glazed inside.

Ht. $9''$ Diam. $4\frac{3}{4}''$
Chekiang celadon
XIV century
Exhib.: OCS 1947 (Celadon), 123 ('Early Ming'); Venice 1954, 439 ('Yüan')
Publ. Gompertz, *Celadon*, Pl. 87 ('Chekiang celadon, early Ming')
The shape is one found in Yüan and early Ming metalwork. This piece has been called Ch'u-chou ware because it has been generally thought until recently that, after the end of the Sung Dynasty, the Lung-ch'üan tradition was transferred to Ch'u-chou; but it is now known that the Lung-ch'üan kilns were active well into the Ming Dynasty

C. 317   Pl. 94b

Small bowl of greyish-white stoneware, decorated inside with spray of prunus incised in the paste under a crackled greenish celadon glaze. Burnt reddish-brown where exposed on bottom of small foot. For use with a stand. Very similar to the bowl with a stand Pl. 92a.

Ht. $1\frac{3}{8}''$ Diam. $4\frac{1}{8}''$
Chekiang celadon
XIII–XIV century

C. 69   Pl. 95a

Pair of ovoid jars with deep covers, of greyish porcellanous stoneware covered with a green celadon glaze. The body is ornamented with peonies freely carved in the paste, above a scalloped band, with a narrower band of peonies round the shoulder. The sides of the covers are also ornamented with peonies, while the top of each bears the character *fu*[1] (happiness) incised under the glaze. The slightly splayed foot is partly glazed, and burnt brown where exposed. Glazed inside the base.

The presence of the character *fu* indicates that these were probably made to be given as birthday presents.

Ht. $7\frac{5}{8}''$ Diam. $4\frac{3}{4}''$
Chekiang celadon
Probably Yüan Dynasty

[1] See p. 157.

98

C. 298   Pl. 95b

Pear-shaped bottle with slender neck and everted mouth, of light greyish porcellanous stoneware, covered inside and out with a green celadon glaze. The decoration, incised in the body under the glaze, is as follows: round upper part of neck, vertical plantain leaves; below this a band of *lei-wen* thunder pattern and a wider band of floral scrolls; the body is decorated with peonies above a band of formalized lotus petals; the high foot has a band of *lei-wen*. The bottom of foot-rim is unglazed.

Ht. $13\frac{1}{2}''$ Diam. $7\frac{3}{4}''$

Chekiang celadon

XIV–XV century

Exhib.: OCS 1947 (Celadon), 125

Cf. Former Alexander coll., Hobson, Rackham and King, *Chinese Ceramics in Private Collections*, p. 7 fig. 8; Pope, *Ardebil*, Pl. 129 ('XIV–XV century'); Venice 1954, 446 ('early XV century')

C. 55   Pl. 95c

Bowl of heavily-potted stoneware on high foot, elaborately decorated with motifs impressed and incised in the paste under a green celadon glaze. Outside around the lip is a band of formalized *lei-wen*; on the body, freely incised floral sprays; inside, in the centre the character *kao*,[1] which is probably a family name; on the side a freize of six figures with inscriptions below a band of formalized *lei-wen*.

Beside four of the figures are inscriptions in cartouches, as follows:

Li Po kuan shu chuan (Li Po reading a book)
Hsiang k'an hua tzu ts'ai (Someone, perhaps Li Po also, looking at a portrait of himself)
K'ung Tzu i Yen Hui (Confucius thinking of Yen Hui)
Chen Tzu an ch'i tsai (Chen Tzu [not identified] playing chess)

Ht. $3\frac{1}{2}''$ Diam. $5\frac{7}{8}''$

Chekiang celadon

XIV–XV century

Exhib.: BH 1935, 1363 ('Perhaps Shouchou ware. Yüan or Ming Dynasty') Manchester 1936, 6455

Publ. Hobson, *Trans. OCS* 1924–25, p. 28 ('Feng-yang celadon')

Cf. Eumo., *Cat.* II, Pl. 34, B. 131, B. 132 ('Probably Yüan'), B. 131 has the character *jen*, benevolence, in centre medallion; rather larger but very similar bowl in George de Menasce coll., London

C. 48   Pl. 96a

Pair of vases, of rectangular section moulded in two halves luted together vertically up the centre of the short sides. Light greyish porcellanous ware covered with a green celadon glaze. The short sides are plain. The long sides of the rectangular body are ornamented in moulded relief with double panels containing the emblem ☰, one of the eight trigrams, against a diapered background. Below are lotus panels separated by a fillet. The slightly

---

[1] See p. 157.

99

flaring neck is adorned with a raised band and with two loop-handles in the form of fishes. The bottom of the foot is unglazed and burnt red; the deep hollow base is glazed.

Ht. $10\frac{1}{8}''$ Diam. $3\frac{1}{4}''$
Chekiang celadon
Probably Ming Dynasty

C. 219   Pl. 96b

Small baluster vase of sturdily-potted porcellanous stoneware, made in three sections luted together, covered with an olive-green celadon glaze. The body is decorated with lotus flowers moulded in relief above a band of lotus petals. The mouth is everted. The foot is slightly splayed, very thick, and unglazed on the bottom showing paste burned brick-red. Glazed inside the deep base.

Ht. $5\frac{5}{8}''$ Diam. $2\frac{7}{8}''$
Chekiang celadon
XIV century

C. 54   Pl. 96c

Bowl of heavily-potted greyish stoneware on a rather high foot, covered with a green celadon glaze. Decorated inside with a lotus flower incised in the paste; in the centre the two characters *shih lin* (stone forest) in raised relief; the outside decorated with vertical striations incised under the glaze. Part of the foot-rim and inside base unglazed and burnt brown. Some incrustation inside base.

Ht. $3''$ Diam. $3\frac{5}{8}''$
Chekiang celadon
Ming Dynasty
I have not been able to discover the significance of the inscription *shih lin*, which may be compared with one on a blue and white shard, reading *shih shan erh*[1] ('stone mountain two'), discovered at Kota Tinggi in Malaya and now in the collection of the Art Museum of the University of Singapore

C. 96   Pl. 97a

Dish of grey porcellanous stoneware with sharply cut everted rim. Decorated round wall with floral scrolls freely incised under a greenish-grey celadon glaze. In the centre three fishes (carp ?) moulded in relief under the glaze. The exterior is fluted, the foot-rim exposed and burnt brown, the base glazed inside.

Ht. $2\frac{7}{8}''$ Diam. $14''$
Ching-te-chen celadon
Ming Dynasty

C. 68   Pl. 97b

Small dish with flat foliated rim, of heavily-potted white porcelain covered with a glassy green celadon glaze. Decorated on rim and in centre with flowers modelled in low relief

[1] See p. 157.

100

under the glaze; the side fluted. The exterior is plain, the bottom of the short thick foot unglazed and burnt reddish-buff. The base is glazed.

Ht. $\frac{3}{4}''$ Diam. $4\frac{1}{4}''$
Ching-te-chen celadon
Early Ming, XV century

C. 258   Pl. 97c

Shallow bulb-bowl, with small slightly concave base, and inverted rim. Standing on three low feet decorated with monster masks. An irregular unglazed patch in the bottom bears a design stamped in the clay, consisting of a central circular medallion containing four characters *li hou ? ts'ang*,[1] within a chequered pattern of squares containing reserved swastikas. The outside is decorated with boldly modelled peonies in relief between two rows of studs in the shape of rosettes. The base is unglazed and bears a short inscription written in ink, of which only the first character, the surname Wang, is legible. White porcelain, burnt reddish-brown where exposed, elsewhere covered with a thick green celadon glaze.

Ht. $4\frac{1}{8}''$ Diam. $12\frac{3}{4}''$
Ching-te-chen celadon
Ming Dynasty, XV century
Cf. Bowl of same family but with *pa-kua* (the eight trigrams) on exterior, Eumo., *Cat.*
    II, Pl. XXXVI, B. 136

C. 57   Pl. 98a

Stem-cup, with flaring octagonal bowl on a round stem. Whitish porcellanous ware. Decorated in centre with peony, round inside lip with broken-down *lei-wen* pattern incised in the paste under a grass-green celadon glaze. The exterior of the bowl is ornamented with flowers on each facet, supported by a band of petals on the underside. The slightly splayed stem has vertical striations beneath a double raised ring. The chamfered foot is partly unglazed revealing the paste burnt reddish-brown; the hollow base is glazed inside.

Ht. $5\frac{1}{8}''$ Diam. $4\frac{3}{4}''$
Ching-te-chen celadon
Ming Dynasty, late XV century

C. 233   Pl. 98b

Vase in the shape of a miniature bronze ritual vessel of the type *fang-hu*; oblong in section, with two tubular handles on the neck. Dark grey stoneware, stained blackish on the foot-rim. Covered with a thick, soft blue-grey *Ju*-type glaze. Said to have been excavated in a well at Hangchow, covered with a white clayey deposit, of which there are traces in the handles.

Ht. $3\frac{1}{4}''$ Diam. $2\frac{1}{4}''$
Ching-te-chen celadon
Probably **XVIII** century

[1] See p. 157.

Exhib.: OCS 1952 (Ju and Kuan), 102 ('XVIII century')

Cf. Octagonal vase with poem by Ch'ien-lung inscribed on the base, Chinese Government coll., BH 1935, 829 ('Chinese attribution : Southern Sung')

C. 264   Pl. 98c

Dish of white porcelain with flat rim, covered with light blue-green celadon glaze. In the centre are two fishes painted in copper-red. The exterior is fluted, the bottom of the foot-rim unglazed.

Ht. $1\frac{5}{8}''$ Diam. $8''$

Ching-te-chen celadon

Probably XVIII century

C. 121   Pl. 99a

Saucer-dish on wide shallow foot, of porcelain covered with a green celadon glaze. An unglazed ring on the base is burnt reddish-brown. Decorated in the centre with a peony surrounded with leaves impressed in the paste under the glaze; another band of peonies encircles the side beneath a narrow scroll band under the rim. Peony scrolls decorate the outside, above a band of formalized *lei-wen* encircling the foot.

Ht. $1\frac{5}{8}''$ Diam. $7\frac{1}{4}''$

Ching-te-chen celadon

Ming Dynasty, XV century

C. 269   Pl. 99b

Deep bowl of heavily-potted whitish porcelain, covered with a green celadon glaze. Decorated inside with waves freely incised in the paste; the centre plain. The outside adorned with incised peonies with a narrow floral band round the rim. On the base, unglazed ring burnt reddish-brown.

Ht. $5\frac{3}{8}''$ Diam. $11\frac{3}{4}''-12\frac{1}{4}''$

Chekiang celadon

Ming Dynasty, XV century

Cf. Bowl with very similar design inside, Pope, *Ardebil*, Pl. 127 ('XV century')

C. 334A   Pl. 100a

Dish with flanged, slightly concave rim. Coarse porcelain. Decorated inside with band of floral scrolls incised in the paste, and impressed flower design in centre, under light greenish celadon glaze. Glaze ends in uneven line above base. Foot-rim bare and burnt brown. Inside base glazed.

Ht. $3\frac{1}{8}''$ Diam. $13\frac{5}{8}''$

Ching-te-chen celadon

XIV–XV century

C. 168   Pl. 100b

Pot or stand, with rounded body, concave base, projecting flange, and slightly tapering neck. Heavily-potted porcellanous body burnt dark brown on exposed base, covered with a very thick light grey crackled glaze, into which several holes have been drilled. Possibly a honey-pot.

Ht. $2\frac{3}{8}''$ Diam. $2\frac{1}{2}''$
Ching-te-chen ware
XVIII century
Cf. Pot of similar shape in David coll., *Cat*. Pl. 137

C. 287 Pl. 100c

Saucer dish, sturdily potted with flat serrated rim, of porcelain, covered with a glassy green glaze with a pronounced crackle stained brown. In the centre and barely visible is a lotus flower within a double circle, incised in the paste under the glaze. The inside of the foot and the base are largely unglazed, stained brown or black, with part of the saggar adhering.

Ht. $1\frac{1}{2}''$ Diam. $6''$
Ching-te-chen celadon
XV century
Exhib.: OCS 1947 (Celadon), 127

C. 318 Pl. 101a

Incense-burner in the shape of a shallow dish on three low feet in the form of monster masks. Six studs are applied round rim. Below, the eight trigrams are rather crudely indicated by three parallel grooves broken by vertical grooves. In fact the arrangement is incorrect, the trigram of three broken lines not being where it should be — i.e. directly opposite the three continuous lines. Hard light buff earthenware covered with an ochre-yellow heavily-crackled glaze. An uneven area in the centre and the base are unglazed.

Ht. $3\frac{3}{4}''$ Diam. $10\frac{7}{8}''$
South China
Ming Dynasty

C. 304 Pl. 101b

Small bowl with cover, of heavily-potted stoneware, covered inside and out with a grey-green to olive glaze in places heavily crackled. The short foot and base are glazed. Some decomposition, probably the result of burial.

Ht. $2\frac{1}{2}''$ Diam. $4''$
South China celadon ware, of a type that has been found in Sarawak
Sung Dynasty
Cf. Pieces excavated at Sungei Ja'ong, Sarawak, Tom Harrisson, 'Some Ceramics
Excavated in Borneo', *Trans. OCS* 1953–54, colour frontispiece

C. 360 Pl. 101c

Dish of heavily-potted porcelain, decorated in centre with incised floral pattern under a celadon glaze. There is an unglazed ring, burnt reddish, inside the base.

Ht. $2\frac{1}{4}''$ Diam. $10\frac{3}{4}''$

South China celadon of a type exported to South-East Asia
XV century

C. 361   Pl. 102a

Dish of heavily-potted stoneware, with flat flanged rim and wide foot, the paste showing dark brown where burnt in unglazed ring inside base. The inside is fluted. Covered with a thick streaked and slightly mottled green glaze which forms a pool at one side and runs to heavy droplets round the base.

Ht. $3\frac{1}{4}''$ Diam. $17\frac{1}{4}''$
South China export ware
Ming Dynasty

C. 302   Pl. 102b

Dish, of heavily-potted stoneware. Decorated round wall with a band of impressed floral decoration under a greenish-grey celadon glaze with a pronounced primary and secondary crackle. Ornament (?) roughly impressed in centre. Low, broad foot; wide unglazed ring burnt reddish-brown in centre of base.

Ht. $3\frac{1}{4}''$ Diam. $16\frac{7}{8}''$
South China export ware
Ming Dynasty

C. 393   Pl. 103a

Large flat dish of heavily-potted whitish porcellanous ware, covered with green celadon glaze. The side is fluted, the flanged lip foliated suggesting lotus petals. The foot is short and rounded and there is an unglazed ring burnt reddish-brown on the base, with portions of round saggar adhering to it in places.

The potting and glaze are of unusually fine quality for a dish of this size.

Ht. $3\frac{7}{8}''$ Diam. $24\frac{5}{8}''$
Ming Dynasty

C. 33   Pl. 103b

Jar of heavily-potted grey stoneware, burnt brick-red on the exposed base. The body is decorated with a diaper pattern on incised parallel lines, forming diamonds in each of which is a little flower; below are vertical grooves suggesting petals, which are repeated on the neck. Round the shoulder are incised six lotus containing a floral motif. The jar is covered with a grass-green celadon glaze, which stops just short of the chamfered foot.

Ht. $8''$ Diam. $5\frac{3}{4}''$
South China export ware
Late Ming Dynasty

12. Ch'ing-Pai *and Related Wares*

It is now generally recognized that the Sung white porcelain decorated with incised or impressed designs under a white glaze with a faint bluish-green tint, known for the last half century as *ying-ch'ing* ('shadowy blue/green'), should be called *ch'ing-pai*, a term to be found in Chinese ceramic literature as early as Southern Sung.

In the present state of our knowledge it is not always possible to distinguish between the white wares of North and South China. It is often said that those from North China kilns show a reddish hue by transmitted light, due to their having been fired in an oxidizing atmosphere, whereas those of Kiangsi, fired under reduction, have a bluish-green tint. While this seems generally to be true, it cannot be confirmed except by careful examination of deposits from a large number of kilns, and indeed Koyama reports that a small proportion of the shards he picked up at the Ting kilns were of a type which would, on this criterion, be labelled Southern. The *ch'ing-pai* wares of South China embrace an enormous family, ranging in date from the T'ang to the Yüan and early Ming, in place of origin from Kiangsi to the coast of Chekiang and Fukien, and in quality from the most delicate and refined to rough grave goods and export wares. That the latter were much in demand abroad is shown by the quantities found in South-East Asia, in India, Southern Arabia and East Africa. The thirteenth-century writer Chao Ju-kua recorded in his *Chu-fan chih* that *ch'ing-pai* was one of the many commodities used by Chinese merchants trading to Java. Elsewhere he notes that should a traveller in the interior of Luzon be waylaid by natives, he had only to leave a piece of porcelain on the path and they would jump down out of the trees, seize it and run off shouting for joy, a reaction with which the modern collector would have much sympathy.

It may be assumed that the finest Sung *ch'ing-pai*, Pls. 110a, 111c and 112c, for example, was made in the region of Ching-te-chen; but pieces of good quality were also made at Chi-chou, and at Kuang-che, in the hills to the north-west of Chienyang. A study of the vast Ching-te-chen industry, recently published in China,[1] gives a chronological list of kilns in the area from T'ang to Ming:

T'ang Dynasty	Shih-hu-wan (also given as Pai-hu-wan)
Five Dynasties	T'ang-hsia; Ying-t'ien
Northern Sung	Hsü-chia-p'ing; T'ang-shan
Northern Sung to Yüan	Niu-shih-ling
Sung Dynasty	Wang-ts'un; Hsiang-hu; Tu-hu-k'ang; Nan-shan
Southern Sung	San-pao-p'eng; Liu-chia-wan; Nan-shih; Ting-ts'un
Yüan Dynasty	Feng-yüan
Yüan-Ming	Yang-mei-ling; Hu-t'ien
Early Ming	Tung-chia-wan

[1] *Ching-te-chen t'ao-tz'u shih-kao* (Draft History of the Pottery and Porcelain of Ching-te-chen), Peking, 1959.

105

Ming Dynasty	Ssu-ch'ien; Ching-te-chen (two main kiln centres: Chu-shan in the northern, and Hsiao-nan in the southern, part of the city); Chu-shan, the imperial factory under the Ming, was started in 1369

It is tempting to assign individual pieces in this collection to one or other of these kilns according to their period, but until we have access to the full range of wares made at each of these kilns, it would be unwise, in spite of Brankston's valuable explorations, to hazard a guess as to precisely what each factory produced.

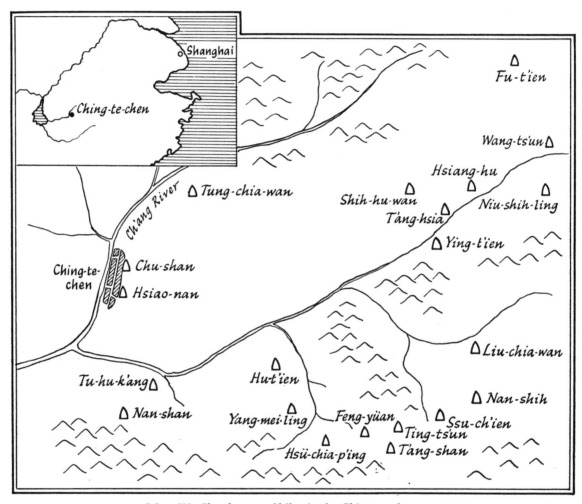

MAP IV. Sketch-map of kilns in the Ching-te-chen area

There is a reference in the eighth-century *Tea Classic* (*Ch'a-ching*) to the ware of Hung-chou, and many attempts have been made to identify it. A bowl in the Tokyo National Museum, decorated inside with a lotus impressed in the paste under a greenish *ch'ing-pai* glaze very similar to the bowl illustrated in Pl. 30a, has been called Hung-chou ware by Komai.[1] However, in a recent article, Chiang Ssu-ch'ing states that so far no T'ang kilns

[1] It is illustrated in *Sekai Tōji Zenshu* IX, Pl. 38 (upper).

106

have been found at Hung-chou, and suggests that the so-called T'ang Hung-chou ware was actually made at Ching-te-chen.[1]

This collection contains, in addition to the fine quality Sung *ch'ing-pai* and its Yüan imperial successor the *Shu-fu* ware, an interesting group of grave jars with moulded decoration under the decomposed glaze. One of them (Pl. 105a), is said to have been found in an imperial tomb of the Posterior Chou (951–60) on Lung-hu-shan in Kiangsu, and others of this group may also be pre-Sung. The two grave-jars illustrated in Pls. 107 and 108a offer an interesting comparison with the same shapes in Chekiang celadon (Pls. 74b and 86a).

C. 376   Pl. 104a

Funerary jar with conical flanged cover. Thickly-potted white porcellanous ware, covered with heavily-crackled pale bluish glaze. Short thick splayed foot. Inside, foot and base unglazed.

Ht. $5\frac{1}{2}''$ Diam. $3''$
Ch'ing-pai ware, probably from Kiangsi
IX–X century

C. 358   Pl. 104b

Funerary jar with cover, of thinly-potted light buff stoneware covered outside with a thin, crackled pale greenish-grey glaze which stops $1\frac{1}{2}''$ short of the base. There are two pairs of small loop-handles on the sharply cut shoulder. The lid has a wide flange, and concentric, sharply cut grooves surrounding a flattened knob. The unglazed base is slightly concave.

Ht. $9\frac{3}{8}''$ Diam. $5\frac{7}{8}''$
Ch'ing-pai type

C. 291   Pl. 104c

Vase of thinly-potted light buff earthenware made in four sections with small handles bearing roughly modelled masks. The pear-shaped body bears a wide band of decoration consisting of a dragon confronting a flaming jewel and a tiger confronting a plant, vigorously modelled in relief under a finely-crackled light greyish-green glaze. The lower part of body and the splayed foot and base are unglazed.

Said to have been 'excavated by Brankston'.

Ht. $8\frac{3}{4}''$ Diam. $5''$
Kiangsi *ch'ing-pai* ware
About X century
Cf. Pair of very similar vases in the coll. of Mr Warren E. Cox ('said to be from Fuliang, north of Ching-te-chen') Los Angeles 1957, 269

C. 294   Pl. 105a

Vase of whitish earthenware, made in two sections luted together, with splayed square lip. Lower half of neck fluted. Upper half of body decorated with small flowers in diaper

---

[1] *Wen-wu* 1958.2, pp. 23–24. The same view is put forward in the *Ching-te-chen t'ao-tz'u shih-kao*, p. 49. Neither, however, attempts to identify it.

pattern. Lower half has half-flowers below raised band, supported by flutings suggesting lotus petals. High hollow base. Covered with pale bluish finely-crackled glaze. Foot, base and interior unglazed.

Said to have come from an imperial tomb of the Posterior Chou Dynasty (906–59) on Lung-hu-shan, Kiangsi.

Ht. 8″   Diam. 4¼″
Kiangsi *ch'ing-pai* ware
X century

C. 297   Pl. 105b

Vase, with depressed globular body, slightly flared neck with square-cut rim, and high hollow flanged foot. Made in three sections luted together. Light brownish-white earthenware. Neck decorated with raised band. On neck, lotus flowers between two lion heads with rings in relief. On body, two bands of formalized flowers in lozenges separated by raised band, above a band of flutings, all in raised relief under a pale finely-crackled blue glaze. Foot, base and interior unglazed.

Ht. 7¾″   Diam. 5″
Kiangsi *ch'ing-pai* ware
IX–XI century

C. 120   Pl. 105c

Jar with cover. Fine white earthenware. Vertical side divided by four hatched straps suggesting cord. Low foot. Light greenish glaze chipped off in places and stained brown. Base and underside of lid unglazed.

Ht. 3⅛″   Diam. 6¼″
Kiangsi *ch'ing-pai* ware
X century
Cf. Eumo., *Cat.* III, Pl. XXIV, C. 117

C. 240   Pl. 106a

Cup on splayed foot. Light buff porcellanous ware. Two handles in the form of dragons whose tails curl over the body of the vessel. Greenish-blue glaze. Rim and heads of dragons unglazed. Splayed foot, base unevenly glazed and stained brown in places.

Ht. 3″   Diam. 4″
Kiangsi *ch'ing-pai* ware
X–XI century
Exhib.: Venice 1954, 570; OCS 1960 (Sung), 203
Cf. Trans. OCS 1945–46, Pl. 21a; Gray, *Early Chinese Pottery and Porcelain*, Pl. 64B; a very similar cup, rather wider in proportion, is in the coll. of Mrs. Alfred Clark, Ht. 3¼″; Kempe coll., Venice 1954, 569, with dragon head glazed

C. 26   Pl. 106b

Pair of vases. Buff-sandy earthenware, made in four sections luted together. Body decorated with bands of lotus plants moulded in relief against background of raised dots separated by a raised band. Above and below are bands of formalized lotus petals. Two lion masks in relief applied to shoulder. Covered with thick light bluish crackled glaze, unevenly applied. High hollow base and foot unglazed. The technique suggests an imitation of metalwork.

Ht. $9\frac{1}{8}''$ Diam. $4\frac{3}{4}''$
Ch'ing-pai ware
X–XI century
Cf. Eumo., *Cat.* II, Pl. XIV, B. 41

C. 230   Pl. 107

Funerary jar. Roughly-potted porcellanous ware. Encircling the shoulder is a dragon moulded in the round, with four horns and long curved snout, grasping balls in three of his four paws. Below, on a ridge of pinched-in paste a baby lies on his stomach looking up; above, under the bulbous lip, a conventional cloud. The conical flanged lid is surmounted by a bird with wings and head upraised. Shallow sharply cut foot-rim. Greenish-blue glaze applied unevenly, running in streaks down to the foot. Base, rim, and underside of lid unglazed.

Ht. $14\frac{1}{2}''$ Diam. $7\frac{1}{2}''$
Ch'ing-pai ware
X–XI century
Exhib.: OCS 1949 (Ting, etc.), 166

C. 72   Pl. 108a

Funerary jar with cover, of fine light grey porcellanous ware, covered inside and out with a pale blue unevenly-crackled glaze, deeper blue-green where it runs thick. From the middle of the three-tiered shoulder rise five spout-shaped holders for incense sticks. The mouth is inverted, the mouth-rim unglazed and burnt light brown. The slightly splayed foot is partially glazed, the base unglazed, unevenly finished and burnt light reddish-brown. The domed lid has a wide flange, and a knob in the form of a dog with head and tail upraised.

Ht. $10''$ Diam. $4\frac{3}{4}''$
Ch'ing-pai ware
Sung Dynasty, probably XI or early XII century

C. 283   Pl. 108b

Shallow bowl on small foot with slightly everted rim. Greyish porcellanous stoneware. Inside a large flower incised in the paste under pale bluish glaze. Exterior plain. Shallow foot, rough unglazed base burnt buff.

Ht. $2\frac{1}{8}''$ Diam. $7\frac{5}{8}''$
Kiangsi *ch'ing-pai* ware
Sung Dynasty, XII–XIII century

C. 339   Pl. 109a

Bowl with six-lobed rim, of fine-grain white slightly translucent porcellanous ware.

Decorated inside with three birds in cartouches, lightly incised in the paste under a pale greyish glaze shading to blue-green where thick, and flecked with black on the outside. Sharply cut foot, unglazed inside base.

Ht. $2\frac{3}{8}''$ Diam. $7\frac{1}{4}''$
Kiangsi *ch'ing-pai* ware
XI–XII century

C. 331   Pl. 109b
Octagonal dish of fine-grained porcellanous ware, covered with a creamy glaze with a greenish tint where it runs thick on the base. Rim unglazed. No foot.

Ht. $\frac{5}{8}''$ Diam. $5\frac{3}{4}''$
Kiangsi *ch'ing-pai* ware
XI–XII century

C. 326   Pl. 109c
Saucer-dish of light buff porcellanous ware. Decorated inside with a band of geometric decoration, below which are alternating flower sprays and formalized flowers moulded in the paste under a pale bluish-green glaze. Rim unglazed. Shallow roughly modelled foot; glazed inside base.

Ht. $1\frac{3}{8}''$ Diam. $5\frac{5}{8}''$
Kiangsi *ch'ing-pai* ware, probably from Chi-an (Yung-ho)
XII–XIII century

C. 19   Pl. 110a
Shallow bowl on small foot, with everted six-foil rim. Translucent white porcellanous stoneware. Floral design incised in the paste inside, under pale bluish glaze; exterior plain. Shallow, sharply cut foot-rim; centre of base unglazed.

Ht. $1\frac{7}{8}''$ Diam. $7''$
Ch'ing-pai ware
Sung Dynasty
Exhib.: BH 1935, 943; Manchester 1936, 6447; Dartington Hall 1949, 69

C. 23   Pl. 110b
Bowl. Whitish porcelain with pale blue glaze. Rim unglazed. Glazed inside base.

Ht. $2\frac{7}{8}''$ Diam. $5\frac{1}{8}''$
Ch'ing-pai ware
Sung Dynasty
Exhib.: BH 1935, 929; Manchester 1936, 6444

C. 102   Pl. 111a
Incense-burner or lamp. White porcellanous ware. Bowl with flat flanged lip, on three-tiered base with grooves under light blue glaze. Hollow base glazed in centre, otherwise unglazed and burnt brown.

Ht. $3\frac{1}{4}''$ Diam. $3''$
Ch'ing-pai ware
Sung Dynasty
Cf. Hoyt, *Cat.* 360, 'incense burner, *Ying-ch'ing* type'; Mrs. Leopold Dreyfus, OCS
1960 (Sung), 199

C. 58 Pl. 111b

Vase of fine light grey earthenware burnt reddish inside base. Tall neck and flaring lip, with two rings modelled in the clay and set in loop-handles issuing from monster heads. The body is decorated with lotus flowers and a flying bird on each side incised under a pale blue glaze. Hollow, slightly flaring flanged base. Foot unglazed; base partly glazed on side.

Ht. $10\frac{3}{8}''$ Diam. $4\frac{7}{8}''$
Ch'ing-pai ware
Sung Dynasty, XIII century
Exhib.: OCS 1949 (Ting, etc.), 35
Cf. Eumo., *Cat.* II, f. 70

C. 24 Pl. 111c

Shallow bowl on small foot, with everted six-foil rim. Translucent white porcellanous stoneware. With design of two fishes among waves incised in the paste inside, under pale bluish glaze; exterior plain. Shallow base; sharply cut foot-rim; centre of base unglazed.

Ht. $2\frac{1}{8}''$ Diam. $7\frac{3}{8}''$
Ch'ing-pai ware
Sung Dynasty
Exhib.: BII 1935, 926; Manchester 1936, 6443; Arts Council 1953, 50

C. 109 Pl. 112a

Conical bowl of translucent white porcelain. Decorated with baby-amid-flowers design inside, and oblique fluting (petals ?) outside under pale blue slightly crackled glaze. High foot, base left unglazed.

Ht. $2\frac{7}{8}''$ Diam. $5\frac{1}{4}''$
Ch'ing-pai ware
Sung Dynasty, XIII century
Exhib.: BH 1935, 934; Manchester 1936, 6446; OCS 1949 (Sung), 110; Arts Council
1953, 51

C. 276 Pl. 112b

Bowl with slightly flanged and everted rim. Heavily-potted porcellanous body, burnt reddish where exposed. Design of a goose sketched in the paste inside, and lotus petals roughly carved outside under pitted thick bluish glaze. Rim unglazed. Very shallow foot-rim and base unglazed.

Ht. $2\frac{1}{4}''$ Diam. $6\frac{3}{8}''$

Ch'ing-pai type, probably made in South China
Sung Dynasty
Exhib.: OCS 1949 (Sung), 92

C. 18   Pl. 112c

Vase. Rounded body, wide mouth with flaring six-lobed lip. Hard white semi-translucent porcelain. Main part of body decorated with floral pattern incised in the paste under pale bluish glaze. High slightly splayed foot, partly unglazed inside base.

Ht. $6\frac{3}{4}''$ Diam. $5\frac{3}{4}''$
Kiangsi *ch'ing-pai* ware
Sung Dynasty
Exhib.: BH 1935, 433; Manchester 1936, 228; OCS 1949 (Ting, etc.) 37; Venice 1954, 560

C. 214   Pl. 113a

Cosmetic box of fine white porcelain, containing a separate tray in which are three small cups separated by branches with flowers. The bluish-white glaze, which covers the exterior and inside bottom of the box and the inside of the tray, has reddish discoloration and is chipped away here and there. Short slightly concave unglazed base.

Ht. $2\frac{3}{4}''$ Diam. $4\frac{3}{4}''$
Ch'ing-pai ware, probably made at Ching-te-chen
X century
Cf. Box, with three small separate boxes similar to C. 336 (Pl. 115a), excavated at Nanking, see *Ching-te-chen t'ao-tz'u shih-kao* (Draft History of the Pottery and Porcelain of Ching-te-chen), 1959, fig. 22
Lacquer box, without the separate tray, but having decorated lid, and of finer workmanship, in Mount Trust, *publ.* OCS 1960 (Sung), 217
With attached dishes, Hoyt, *Cat.* 376
A moulded Korean box of this type *publ.* by Honey, 'Corean Wares of the Koryŏ Period', *Trans. OCS* 1946–47, Pl. 5e
An inlaid Korean one, in the coll. of G. St. G. M. Gompertz, is illustrated in his 'Koryŏ Inlaid Celadon Wares', *Trans. OCS* 1953–54, Pl. 17c
A Lung-ch'üan celadon example Eumo., *Cat.* II, Pl. XXIV B. 133; see also *ch'ing-pai* box in *Ibid.*, Pl. IV, B. 10
A Ting ware piece with five little boxes inside, in the Tokyo National Museum, is illustrated in *Sekai Tōji Zenshu* X, fig. 73

This box was shown at an OCS Specimen Meeting by A. L. Hetherington, and is reproduced as 18a of the *Trans. OCS* for 1942–43. On the same plate, 18b, he illustrated a modern Burmese betel box of Pagan lacquer, the upper tray of which contains three little silver bowls, a pot for chunam (lime), and a nutcracker to split the areca nut.

C. 169   Pl. 113b

Bowl of translucent white porcelain, on very short foot. Decorated inside with phoenixes

112

and peonies beneath key-fret border; in the centre is a lotus plant impressed in the paste under a pale bluish glaze. Bottom of foot and rim unglazed. Rim sheathed in copper.

Ht. $3\frac{1}{2}''$ Diam. $7\frac{3}{8}''$
Kiangsi *ch'ing-pai* ware
Sung Dynasty
Exhib.: OCS 1949 (Sung), 120 ('Resembling Ting ware in potting and design, but with *ying-ch'ing* type glaze'); Arts Council 1953, 53

C. 90   Pl. 113c

Shallow bowl on small foot, with everted six-foil rim. Translucent white porcellanous stoneware. Peonies incised in the paste inside, under pale bluish glaze; exterior plain. Shallow base; sharply cut foot-rim; centre of base unglazed. The character *ch'ien*[1] has been written on the base in recent times.

Ht. $2\frac{3}{8}''$ Diam. $7\frac{3}{4}''$
Ch'ing-pai ware
Sung Dynasty

C. 193   Pl. 114a

Basket-shaped jar with globular body, short neck and wide everted mouth, and small flat base. Hard grey stoneware decorated with combed pattern on body, and a row of twenty-nine small pointed bosses round the neck between bands of incised lines. Covered inside and on lip with brownish-black glaze, splashed here and there on the body. The bosses round the neck are covered with a grey glaze.

Ht. $4\frac{1}{4}''$ Diam. $5''$
Kiangsi, made in Ching-te-chen area, probably at Nan-shan
Sung Dynasty
Exhib.: OCS 1952 (Chün and Brown), 128; Arts Council 1953, 39; Musée Cernuschi 1956
Cf. Jar formerly in Eumorfopoulos coll., Ht. $3\frac{1}{2}''$, *illus.* Brankston, 'An Excursion to Ching-te-chen', *Trans. OCS* 1938–39, Pl. 4a ('?XI–XII century'); slightly larger jar in Percival David Foundation, No. 323

C. 319   Pl. 114b

Pot with globular body, straight neck and slightly everted rim, a row of bosses round base of neck. Body incised with parallel lines to suggest basket-work. Whitish rough porcellanous ware. Upper half and interior covered with light bluish crackled glaze.

Ht. $3\frac{1}{4}''$ Diam. $3\frac{7}{8}''$
Kiangsi *ch'ing-pai* ware
XIII–XIV century

C. 20   Pl. 114c

Pot with globular body, short neck and slightly everted lip. Thick porcelain. Body

---

[1] See p. 157.

ncised with parallel lines suggesting basket-work under pale blue glaze. Row of brown iron-spots round lower part of neck. Small flat base bearing traces of saggar.

Ht. $3\frac{1}{8}''$ Diam. $4\frac{1}{8}''$
Ch'ing-pai type
XIII–XIV century
Exhib.: OCS 1949 (Sung), 80; Arts Council 1953, 52

C. 336 Pl. 115a
Box with cover, on short foot. Translucent white porcellanous ware. Top of lid decorated with peony moulded in the paste. Sides fluted. Covered with bluish glaze. Inside partly glazed; lower part of body, foot and slightly concave base unglazed.

Ht. $1\frac{3}{4}''$ Diam. $2\frac{1}{2}''$
Ching-te-chen *ch'ing-pai* ware
Sung Dynasty
Exhib.: Musée Cernuschi, 1956

C. 277 Pl. 115b
Covered box of fine-grained white porcellanous ware. The cover decorated with two phoenixes moulded in relief under a creamy-white glaze. Centre of underside of cover, interior of lower half and upper part of side of base also glazed, the latter ending in an uneven line. Flat, rather roughly finished base. Both the shape and the design of this box are derived from T'ang repoussé silver-ware.

Ht. $1\frac{1}{2}''$ Diam. $3\frac{7}{8}''$
Kiangsi *ch'ing-pai* ware, probably made at Chi-an (Yung-ho)
Sung Dynasty
Cf. Sekai Tōji Zenshu X, p. 220, fig. 82 ('N. Sung *ying-ch'ing*')

C. 303 Pl. 115c
Box in the form of an incense-burner. White porcellanous ware. Floral design incised and cut through lid. Body and centre of underside of lid covered with pale bluish glaze. The shape is copied from a censer in openwork bronze, already in use in the T'ang Dynasty.

Ht. $2\frac{1}{4}''$ Diam. $2\frac{1}{8}''$
Kiangsi *ch'ing-pai* ware
Sung Dynasty
Exhib.: OCS 1949 (Ting, etc.), 4 ('Perfume box')
Cf. Hoyt, *Cat.* 379; *Sekai Tōji Zenshu* X, Colour Pl. 3; Gyllensvärd, *T'ang Gold and Silver*, fig. 11, 32, Pls. 1e, 5d, 15c

C. 309 Pl. 115d
Bowl of hard fine light stoneware, with decoration of barely recognizable babies amid lotus leaves, sketchily incised on the inside under pale grey-green glaze. Exterior plain. Foot-rim cut square; base unglazed.

Ht. $2\frac{1}{4}''$ Diam. $6\frac{7}{8}''$

CH'ING-PAI AND RELATED WARES

Kiangsi *ch'ing-pai* ware
Sung Dynasty

C. 206   Pl. 116a

Vessel in the shape of a miniature bronze *ting* on three legs, with two handles projecting above moulded rim. A crackled white glaze with a faint bluish tint covers the body outside; the inside, centre of base and bottom of feet are unglazed.

Ht. $3\frac{5}{8}''$ Diam. $4''$
Ching-te-chen ware
XIII–XIV century

C. 248   Pl. 116b

Ting-tripod. Light grey porcellanous ware, heavily potted. Three curved legs, two handles projecting above rim. Thick lightly-crackled pale blue glaze. Centre of base unglazed.

Ht. including handles $3\frac{1}{8}''$ Diam. $4\frac{1}{8}''$
Ching-te-chen ware
XIII–XIV century

C. 293   Pl. 116c

Saucer-dish. Whitish rather heavily-potted porcellanous ware. Decorated with three fishes amid waves, surrounded by a band of water plants, with a beaded outer border, moulded in the paste under a pale blue glaze. Rim unglazed. Short square-cut foot-rim and base partly glazed.

Ht. $1\frac{1}{2}''$ Diam. $6\frac{3}{4}''$
Kiangsi *ch'ing-pai* type
XIII–XIV century

C. 279   Pl. 117a

Bowl, transparent white porcellanous stoneware. Floral design incised in the paste outside, under pale bluish glaze; interior plain. Rim unglazed. Shallow foot-rim. Glazed inside base.

Ht. $2\frac{1}{4}''$ Diam. $6\frac{1}{2}''$
Ching-te-chen *ch'ing-pai* ware
XIII–XIV century

C. 288   Pl. 117b

Hexagonal box with cover, on small moulded foot, of hard earthenware. Spray of prunus moulded on the lid. Greenish-blue finely-crackled *ch'ing-pai*-type glaze covers lid and upper half of body, and is splashed over part of inside of both halves.

Ht. $1\frac{5}{8}''$ Diam. $2\frac{3}{4}''$
Ch'ing-pai ware, from South China
X–XI century

C. 14   Pl. 117c

Conical bowl on small foot. Translucent white porcellanous ware. Decorated inside with two phoenixes under scroll band, moulded under light blue glaze. Traces of fluting round outside above base. Low roughly finished foot, rim and base unglazed.

Ht. $2\frac{1}{4}''$ Diam. $6\frac{3}{4}''$

Kiangsi *ch'ing-pai* ware

Late Sung or Yüan Dynasty, XIII–XIV century

Exhib.: Venice 1954, 573

C. 97   Pl. 118a

Bowl of translucent white porcelain on a short foot. Decorated inside with a moulded design of peonies under a cream glaze. In three of the leaves near the upper border, reading from right to left, are the characters *Wu Ming-chih*,[1] evidently a person's name. The outside is decorated with freely carved grooves suggesting lotus petals. The glaze outside is of a pale greyish-white with a greenish tint where it runs thick. The unglazed rim is bound in copper. A detail of the base is shown in Pl. 144b.

Ht. $2\frac{3}{8}''$ Diam. $7\frac{3}{8}''$

Kiangsi *ch'ing-pai* ware

XIII century

C. 268   Pl. 118b

Dish with slightly concave base and curving side, of white porcellanous ware. In the centre a goose with outspread wings amid lotus plants; on the side a diaper of cloud-collar motifs under a border of key frets, moulded under a white glaze with a faint bluish-green tint. Unglazed rim with traces of metal band. Very low foot, glazed inside the base. 'Said to have been excavated at Nanchang.'

Ht. $1''$ Diam. $5\frac{5}{8}''$

Kiangsi *ch'ing-pai* type, probably made at Chi-an (Yung-ho)

XIII or XIV century

C. 313   Pl. 118c

Jar with cover. Whitish porcellanous ware. Lines at neck and waist incised under pale bluish glaze. Lid has small loop-handle and floral pattern incised under the glaze. Chamfered foot, slightly chipped. Rim and inside and bottom of foot of jar, and underside of lid flange unglazed.

Ht. $5\frac{1}{4}''$ Diam. $4\frac{1}{2}''$

Ch'ing-pai ware

The lid appears to be from a Sung *ch'ing-pai* piece; the body is cut down, and probably dates from the XIV–XV century

C. 301   Pl. 119a

Shallow bowl of whitish porcelain with very short foot. Decorated inside with six panels

[1] See p. 157.

of alternating lotus plants in shallow trays and peonies in pear-shaped vases, below a key-fret border; in the centre is a lotus panel; all impressed in the paste under a pale yellowish-grey glaze with a greenish tint where it runs thick. Glaze stops short of the rim, with an uneven line on the outside. Two details of the decoration are shown.

Ht. $1\frac{1}{2}''$ Diam. $7''$
Kiangsi *ch'ing-pai* ware
XIII–XIV century

C. 156   Pl. 119b

Bowl of coarse whitish porcelain, with incised and combed floral design inside, and covered outside with curved oblique fluting, under pale bluish-green crackled glaze. Base unglazed except for small splashes. Uneven surface.

Ht. $3''$ Diam. $6\frac{5}{8}''$
Kiangsi *ch'ing-pai* ware
Yüan or early Ming Dynasty

C. 208   Pl. 119c

Bowl of white fine-grained porcelain with pale bluish-grey glaze. Unglazed rim. Shallow foot-rim, glazed inside base.

Ht. $2\frac{1}{4}''$ Diam. $6\frac{3}{4}''$
Kiangsi *ch'ing-pai* ware
XIV–XV century

C. 17   Pl. 120a

Jar with cover. Hard white porcellanous ware. Covered with creamy bluish-white glaze slightly crackled on cover. Rim, inside cover and slightly concave chamfered base unglazed. The four characters *wen wei nan lou*[1] (to be placed in the Southern Pavilion) are written in faded black ink inside the cover.

Ht. $6\frac{7}{8}''$ Diam. $6\frac{1}{4}''$
Ching-te-chen ware, *Shu-fu* type
Yüan Dynasty
Exhib.: Venice 1954, 585

C. 207   Pl. 120b

Pair of bowls, transparent white porcelain, decorated in raised slip under pale bluish glaze. On outside a design of fishes amid waves and water plants; in the centre a crab and waves. Rim stained brown to simulate metal. Bottom of foot-rim unglazed. Deep hollow base glazed inside.

Ht. $1\frac{1}{2}''$ Diam. $2\frac{3}{8}''$
Ching-te-chen ware, *Shu-fu* type
XIV century

[1] See p. 157.

C. 108   Pl. 121a

Pair of bowls. White porcelain, decorated inside with two flying geese amid formalized clouds, beneath a narrow band of scrolls, executed in raised slip under a pale bluish glaze. The character *fu*[1] (happiness) and *lu* (prosperity) on opposite sides. The outside is decorated with scrolls around the rim and five formalized lotus panels incised in the paste. High foot-rim, cut square. Bottom of foot and inside base unglazed.

Ht. $3\frac{3}{4}''$ Diam. $8''$

Ching-te-chen ware, *Shu-fu* type

Yüan Dynasty

Exhib.: BH 1935, 479; Manchester 1936, 6456; Venice 1954, 579; OCS 1957 (Ming), 87

Publ. John Ayers, 'Some Chinese Wares of the Yüan Dynasty', *Trans. OCS* 29 (1954–55), 77–78 and figs. 13 and 14

Cf. Gray, *Early Chinese Pottery and Porcelain*, p. 45 and Pl. 95; this bowl has an inscription in the Phagspa script which was promulgated by Kubilai and was popular for a short time

C. 94   Pl. 121b

Bowl. White porcelain, decorated on the inside in raised slip with design of three storks amid lotus plants over conventionalized waves. Above, a narrow band of scroll pattern; below, a band of chevrons. In the centre, a single stork with waves and lotus plants. Rim stained to imitate metal binding. Bottom of foot-rim unglazed; glazed inside hollow base.

Ht. $1\frac{1}{8}''$ Diam. $3\frac{1}{2}''$

Ching-te-chen ware, *Shu-fu* type

Yüan Dynasty

C. 184   Pl. 121c

Stem-cup with bowl and thick pedestal. Sugary white porcellanous paste. Petals moulded round lower half of bowl under fine pale blue glaze. Flat base partly discoloured.

This piece is said to have been excavated at Ch'ing-ho-hsien.

Ht. $3\frac{3}{8}''$ Diam. $3''$

Ching-te-chen ware

Late Ming or early Ch'ing Dynasty

[1] See p. 157.

13. Southern Black Wares
of the Sung Dynasty

Chi-an ware

In the Chi-an district of Kiangsi there is a popular saying, 'first we had Yung-ho, then came Ching-te-chen'. This suggests that before the huge factories at Ching-te-chen absorbed all the minor kilns in the district or put them out of business, Yung-ho (or Chi-an or Chi-chou, as it was later called) was an important ceramic centre. It was briefly visited by Brankston one rainy day in June 1937. He picked up some shards on the ground and fragments and wasters were brought to him in the village teashop. A much more thorough investigation was carried out by Chiang Hsüan-i and reported in 1957. Altogether twenty-one kilnsites were located in and around the town. It appears that they saw their greatest activity from the tenth to the twelfth century, and finally ceased production during the T'ien-hsien era (1236–82). It seems probable that the potters then migrated to Ching-te-chen.

According to Chiang Hsüan-i, five distinct kinds of ware were made at Chi-chou:

Celadon of three types: 1, coarse and primitive; 2, finely crackled; 3, Lung-ch'üan type.
White porcelain: 1, with a thin white glaze; 2, with moulded decoration under a white glaze, imitating Ting-yao; 3, fine white porcelain with a crackled 'ash-white' glaze. The last two categories were evidently much admired by Ch'ien-lung; and there are examples of both types in the palace collection.
Painted stoneware, decorated in imitation of Tz'u-chou ware.
Black-glazed ware of *temmoku* type (see below).
Green-glazed ware.

A few very coarse pieces of blue and white were also found in the kilnsites, though not sufficient to warrant any conclusion being drawn about its manufacture there.

As this list shows, much of the output of the Chi-chou kilns imitated the famous wares of Hopei, Honan and Chekiang. Even the black-glazed tea-bowls, of which there are three in this collection, are copies of Fukien *temmoku*. But here it seems that the Chi-chou potters made their one original, if modest, contribution. Though roughly potted and poorly glazed, these bowls are adorned with a variety of flowers and plants, phoenixes and auspicious mottoes such as *ch'ang ming fu kuei* or *chin yü man t'ang* in black against the reddish-brown mottled glaze. Chiang Hsüan-i has shown that some of the designs (Pl. 123c for example) were painted in white slip under the glaze; others were produced not by painting, as Brankston and others supposed, but by reserving or printing on the glaze with paper cut-outs, probably steeped in vinegar, which seem to have prevented the mottled effect from developing, leaving that area black. The decoration of these bowls (for example Pl. 122a, b & c) shows, incidentally, that the art of the paper-cut, now undergoing a vigorous revival in China, is at least as old as the Sung Dynasty.

It seems likely that this simple technique for decorating pottery survived in South China, for there is a class of rough late Ming and early Ch'ing export ware found throughout

119

South-East Asia, which has an unglazed ring in the bottom and is decorated round the side with seals, phoenixes, fishes and other devices in bluish-black under a dull bluish-white glaze. It is known in the Philippines as 'Singapore ware', but was probably made in Kwangtung or Fukien.

Chiang Hsüan-i also found wasters of the type of the pair of beautiful jars one of which is illustrated in Pl. 123b. They seem to have been decorated as follows: the vessel was first covered rather unevenly with a white slip over which was laid a thick black glaze; this was then wiped or scraped off to give the shape of the prunus, the twigs being incised in the paste to give a sharp line. The stamens were then lightly touched in over the slip with a brush, and finally covered with a thin transparent glaze.

Fukien *Temmoku*

The sombre dignity of the Fukien *temmoku* is well represented here. Its source among the cloudy, rain-soaked hills of Northern Fukien was discovered by the late James Marshall Plumer in 1935, and has become even better known through the work of later Chinese and Japanese investigators. The huge mounds of shards and wasters marking the ancient kilns to north and east of the town of Chien-ning (formerly Chien-an or Ou-ning), bear witness to an enormous output which served not only the local market, but also that of Japan; for, as every collector knows, the deep rich glaze set off to perfection the cloudy pea-green colour of the tea used in the tea-ceremony. The sturdy stoneware body is almost black, the glaze applied so thick that it streaks and congeals in heavy drops round the foot, or forms deep pools in the bottom. Brilliant effects known as hare's fur (Pl. 124a) and oil-spot were produced when the ferric oxide in the glaze partly crystallized out in the cooling.

Recent investigations by Chinese archaeologists have revealed that *temmoku* was not only made in the Chien-yang kilns discovered by Plumer. In April 1955 an extensive kilnsite was discovered at Kuang-che, on the Fukien-Kiangsi border north-west of Chien-yang (some maps place it just inside Fukien, others in Kiangsi). Shards found there include a black glazed ware, a ware black outside and mottled yellow inside very similar to Chi-chou ware, and a *ch'ing-pai* with carved decoration under the glaze. Inferior versions of *temmoku* (as well as *ch'ing-pai*) were turned out in kilns discovered in 1958 at Pan-ts'en-yao, at the east gate reservoir of Fu-ch'ing, south of Foochow, which also made a celadon with incised decoration of a type widely exported to South-East Asia. The kilns at Nan-an just inland from Ch'üan-chou, investigated in 1957, are reported as having made a wide variety of wares during the Sung Dynasty, including a small quantity of *temmoku*.

C. 98   Pl. 122a

Conical tea-bowl on short foot. Buff stoneware, covered except for the base with a reddish-brown slip. Outside, the black glaze stops well short of the base; the inside is covered with a crackled, finely-mottled cream, blue and brown glaze, with six-petalled flowers reserved in black.

Ht. $2\frac{1}{2}''$ Diam. $4\frac{7}{8}''$

Chi-an ware
Exhib.: Venice 1954, 492 ('Chi-an Temmoku')

C. 117   Pl. 122b

Tea-bowl on short foot. Buff stoneware covered inside with a mottled greenish-brown glaze, with scattered plum-blossoms reserved in black glaze. The outside is covered with a black glaze over a brown slip, stopping halfway down the body in a waving line.

Ht. $2\frac{5}{8}''$ Diam. $4\frac{5}{8}''$
Chi-an ware

C. 103   Pl. 122c

Tea-bowl on short foot. Buff stoneware, covered with a rich brown glaze over a thin brown slip. The glaze is flecked inside with cream and blue streaked glaze, with four motifs, possibly monograms, crudely reserved in the glaze. The brown glaze outside is splashed with greenish-cream, ending on, and short of, the base in an uneven line.

Ht. $2\frac{3}{8}''$ Diam. $5''$
Chi-an ware

C. 316   Pl. 123a

Shallow conical bowl on shallow foot. Roughly potted, fine-grained light grey-buff stoneware, covered with an uneven black glaze, mottled brown. Decorated inside with a flower spray reserved in black and spotted with a thick cream glaze.

Ht. $1\frac{3}{4}''$ Diam. $5\frac{3}{4}''$
Chi-an ware

C. 196   Pl. 123b

Pair of ovoid vases with short neck, thickened lip and very shallow foot. Buff porcellanous stoneware covered with a thick matt brownish-black glaze. On either side a spray of prunus reserved in the biscuit, the stamens painted in brown under a transparent glaze. Said to have been 'excavated', presumably from a tomb.

Ht. $7\frac{7}{8}''$ and $7\frac{1}{2}''$ Diam. $4\frac{3}{4}''$ and $4\frac{1}{2}''$
Chi-an ware
Exhib.: Venice 1954, 494; OCS 1960 (Sung), 194
Cf. Hoyt, *Cat.* 337, 338 ('XIII century'), different shapes, but similar technique and
decoration

C. 99   Pl. 123c

Tea-bowl with slightly everted lip on short straight foot. Coarse light buff stoneware which is exposed on the base, and covered with a rough chocolate-brown slip on the unglazed portion of the outside and foot. Matt brownish-black glaze, the inside decorated with formalized phoenixes and flowers painted in cream slip against a black background.

Ht. $2\frac{1}{8}''$ Diam. $4\frac{1}{2}''$
Chi-an ware

C. 290   Pl. 123d

Deep bowl with slightly everted lip and straight square-cut foot. Light buff, rather heavily potted stoneware covered with a lustrous black glaze mottled brown over a brown slip, and splashed inside and out with streaks of light yellowish-buff glaze. The shallow base is unglazed.

The bowl has been broken and restored.

Ht. 3″   Diam. $6\frac{1}{2}$″

Chi-an ware

Exhib.: OCS 1952 (Chün and Brown), 149

C. 263   Pl. 124a

Tea-bowl; conical, with slightly everted rim, short square-cut foot and shallow base. Brownish-grey stoneware, covered with a thick black glaze streaked with brown 'hare's fur' markings, ending in heavy drops around the base.

Ht. $2\frac{5}{8}$″   Diam. $6\frac{1}{8}$″

Chien ware

Exhib.: OCS 1952 (Chün and Brown), 174; OCS 1960 (Sung), 195

C. 10   Pl. 124b

Conical bowl with slightly inverted mouth, on small slightly splayed and concave base. Heavily-potted grey stoneware covered with a thick lustrous black glaze streaked olive-brown round the rim, and running down into heavy drops, to expose a purple slip.

Ht. $3\frac{3}{4}$″   Diam. $5\frac{3}{4}$″

Chien ware

Exhib.: Dartington Hall 1949, 102; OCS 1952 (Chün and Brown), 176; Musée Cernuschi 1956

C. 322   Pl. 125a

Conical bowl of reddish-brown stoneware with short shallow foot; covered with a 'hare's fur' black glaze flecked with brown.

Ht. 2″   Diam. $5\frac{7}{8}$″

Chien ware

C. 157   Pl. 125b

Conical tea-bowl, with indentation below the rim and short foot with shallow base. Dark stoneware covered with black glaze, ending well short of the base. The rim is bound in silver. Inside are painted in silver four medallions containing the characters *shou shan fu hai*[1] '[may your] life [be as long as] the hills, [your] prosperity [as vast as] the ocean', against a striated background suggesting hare's fur. In the centre a roughly sketched blossom.

Made as a birthday present.

Ht. $2\frac{3}{8}$″   Diam. $5\frac{1}{8}$″

Chien ware

Exhib.: Arts Council 1953, 36

[1] See p. 157.

14. Later Wares

C. 31   Pl. 126a

Tall slender vase with gently curving neck and slightly flaring mouth, on a deep foot. Heavily-potted light buff stoneware, covered with a thick creamy-white crackled 'orange-peel' glaze. Glazed inside base.

Ht. $16\frac{1}{4}''$ Diam. $6''$
'Kiangnan Ting' ware, also called Dongkhe ware
XIII–XV century
Exhib.: BH 1935, 1265
Publ. Hetherington, *Early Ceramic Wares*, Pl. XXII ('XII–XV century'); Honey, *Ceramic Art of China*, Pl. 59 ('Probably Ming')
Cf. Eumo., *Cat.* III, Pl. 30, C. 228

C. 61   Pl. 126b

Rectangular vase imitating shape of bronze *ts'un* of Warring States period. Two square loops for handles on short sides; two raised ridges on shoulder. Made of grey stoneware in two parts luted together, and covered with crackled ivory glaze. Two holes for cord on short sides of base.

Ht. $4''$ Diam. $3''$
Possibly Fukien ware
Ming Dynasty

C. 261   Pl. 126c

Bowl in the shape of a bronze *kuei*, with rounded body, short neck, flanged rim and two square loop-handles. Fine-grain whitish porcellanous stoneware, covered with a finely-crackled ivory glaze stained brown in places. Broad shallow foot, base, and interior unglazed.

Ht. $2\frac{1}{4}''$ Diam. $3\frac{1}{2}''$
Fukien white ware
Ming Dynasty

C. 223   Pl. 126d

Bottle of heavily-potted sandy porcellanous stoneware. Vitreous crackled ivory glaze, shading to greyish at lip and foot. Partly glazed inside base. Bottom of foot-rim unglazed.

Ht. $5\frac{3}{4}''$ Diam. $1\frac{1}{2}''$
Fukien, Dongkhe ware
XVII–XVIII century

C. 15   Pl. 127a

Deep cup on high slightly splayed hollow foot. Hard white porcellanous stoneware, covered with thick ivory finely-crackled glaze. Glazed inside foot and on base, but not on foot-rim.

Ht. $4\frac{3}{4}''$ Diam. $3\frac{7}{8}''$

Fukien white ware, possibly from Dongkhe. Mr. Koyama has suggested that it might be Satsuma ware of the early Edo period (XVII century). The shape, in either case, is unusual

Ming Dynasty

C. 167   Pl. 127b

Jar with globular body, long slender neck and bulbous mouth standing on a short square-cut foot. Hard, fine light buff porcellanous stoneware, covered with a crackled cream glaze. The inside of the base is glazed. The neck is decorated with incised palm leaves above and below a central stamped band of formalized *lei-wen* applied with a roller. Faintly visible round the neck is a band of small incised cloud-collars, while the body is decorated on one side with incised peonies and bamboos above a band of formalized waves which completely encircle the body above the foot.

Ht. $16\frac{1}{2}''$ Diam. $8\frac{1}{8}''$

Fukien Dongkhe ware

Ming Dynasty

C. 107   Pl. 127c

Dish with cusped rim. Heavily potted in porcellanous light buff stoneware, covered with a crackled ivory glaze partly discoloured. Foot-rim unglazed.

Ht. $1\frac{7}{8}''$ Diam. $12''$

Fukien Dongkhe ware

Ming Dynasty

Exhib.: Manchester 1936, 1913

C. 353   Pl. 128a

Potiche of white porcellanous ware, with high shoulder and slightly thickened rim. Covered with a crackled ivory glaze. Foot-rim unglazed.

Ht. $4\frac{3}{8}''$ Diam. $7''$

Fukien white ware

Ming Dynasty

C. 89   Pl. 128b

Conical bowl with slightly everted rim and small foot, of hard greyish-white stoneware. Outside decorated with lightly incised floral scrolls above a band of formalized lotus petals; around the rim outside, a scalloped border containing cloud-collars. Covered with creamy-white finely crackled glaze with the texture of orange-skin. Bottom of foot-rim unglazed.

Ht. $2\frac{1}{8}''$ Diam. $6\frac{3}{4}''$

Fukien Dongkhe ware

XVII or XVIII century

C. 262   Pl. 128c

Bottle with pear-shaped body, long neck and flaring lip. Of whitish stoneware burnt reddish-brown on exposed foot-rim. Baby dragon with raised head modelled in appliqué round the neck, its tail trailing down over the body. Whitish finely-crackled glaze with faint bluish-green tint.

Ht. $5\frac{1}{2}''$ Diam. $2\frac{3}{4}''$
Fukien white ware
XVII—XVIII century
Cf. Similar bottle in Te-hua porcelain in V. & A., Honey, *Ceramic Art of China*, Pl. 142 ('XVIII century')

C. 130   Pl. 129a

Vase, with globular body and slightly everted mouth. Two ring-handles on clasps applied to the shoulder. White porcellanous body made in three sections luted together. Body decorated with peonies incised in the paste; on the shoulder incised whorls in scalloped border; below, a band of lotus petals. Vertical palm-leaves decorate the neck, while the foot bears a band of squared scrolls. The vessel is covered with a creamy Ting-type glaze with a faint greenish tint over a white slip. The rim is bound in copper, the bottom of the shallow foot unglazed.

Ht. $12\frac{1}{4}''$ Diam. $8\frac{7}{8}''$
A South China imitation of Ting ware
XIV century

C. 260   Pl. 129b

Incense-burner in the shape of a *ting* tripod on three legs with lion masks and feet, deeply incised at point where the legs join the body. *Lei-wen* band encircling the shoulder and on outside of loop-handles, under minutely-crackled ivory glaze.

Ht. $4''$ Diam. $3\frac{1}{4}''$
South China
Ch'ing Dynasty

C. 119   Pl. 130a

Deep dish with flattened foliate rim. Porcelain, decorated in underglaze blue, burnt uneven reddish-buff on the unglazed base. The rim is decorated with scrolling vines and fungus; in the moulded sections of the cavettos are twelve separate floral sprays including chrysanthemum, morning glory, peony and lotus; in the centre are five large blossoms and four smaller ones connected by scrolling vines; they include lotus and peony. Outside are twelve floral sprays. A good example of a well-known type.

Ht. $2\frac{7}{8}''$ Diam. $14\frac{7}{8}''$
Ching-te-chen ware
Ming Dynasty, early XV century
Cf. Pope, *Ardebil*, Pl. 35

C. 123   Pl. 130b

Pair of *mei-p'ing* vases, decorated round the body with peonies, above a band of clouds, with cloud-collars round the shoulder. The coarse white porcelain body is made in two sections, the decoration carried out in cobalt blue under a bluish-white crackled glaze.

Ht. $5\frac{7}{8}''$ Diam. $3\frac{7}{8}''$
South China
Ming Dynasty, early XV century

C. 140   Pl. 131a

Dish with flattened rim. Porcelain, decorated in underglazed blue. The rim has a wave design; the cavetto has a scroll of eleven flowers; in the centre are four larger flowers, hibiscus, peony and two camellias, and three smaller ones, connected by scrolling vines. Outside are floral scrolls.

Ht. $2\frac{3}{4}''$ Diam. $16\frac{1}{8}''$
Ching-te-chen ware
Ming Dynasty, early XV century
Cf. Almost identical dishes *illus.* and discussed in Pope, *Ardebil*, Pls. 34, 29, 88, and
     pp. 90–94

C. 383   Pl. 131b

Deep dish with flattened rim; porcelain, decorated in underglazed blue, the cobalt having a particularly rich violet colour. The rim is decorated with waves; round the cavetto is a floral band with twelve blossoms representing eight different flowers; in the centre are three bunches of grapes with leaves and tendrils on a vine. Outside are twelve blossoms connected by scrolling vines.

Ht. $2\frac{3}{4}''$ Diam. $14\frac{3}{4}''$
Ching-te-chen ware
Ming Dynasty, early XV century
Cf. A very similar dish, Pope, *Ardebil*, No. 29.52, Pl. 38; dish in Brodie Lodge coll.,
     OCS 1946 (Blue and White), 40

C. 226   Pl. 132a

Mei-p'ing vase with spreading foot. White porcelain, decorated in underglaze blue round the shoulder with flowers in panels and with a band of formalized lotus petals round the base. The main body is plain, and covered with a thick transparent glaze which has run down in heavy drops over the lower band of decoration; it shows some decomposition probably due to burial. Not of high quality, but an interesting early piece.

Ht. $9\frac{5}{8}''$ Diam. $5\frac{1}{4}''$
Ching-te-chen ware
Late XIV century

C. 154   Pl. 132b

Bowl with everted lip. White porcelain covered with a rich copper-red glaze paling to

126

white at the rim and bottom of the foot. Hsüan-te reign-mark incised under transparent glaze inside base.

Ht. $2\frac{1}{4}''$ Diam. $4\frac{7}{8}''$
Cheng-te-chen ware
Ming Dynasty, Hsüan-te period
Exhib.: OCS 1948 (Monochromes), 73; OCS 1957 (Ming), 102

C. 224   Pl. 132c

Deep bowl with slightly everted lip bound in copper, on a rather high straight foot with shallow base. White porcelain covered with a thick glassy brownish-black glaze, over a brown slip applied in two coats to give the appearance of dark *temmoku* body. The black glaze stops in a thick uneven welt short of the foot.

Ht. $3\frac{5}{8}''$ Diam. $8\frac{1}{8}''$
Ching-te-chen imitation of Honan black ware
Probably K'ang-hsi period, XVII–XVIII century
Cf. Very similar bowl with white porcelain body and glossy black glaze in Percival
    David Foundation, 315 ('Sung')

C. 87   Pl. 133a

Bowl with slightly everted lip. Translucent white porcelain. Decorated with two dragons, and clouds in *an-hua* (concealed decoration) technique under transparent white glaze with faint bluish tint. Marked inside base with Yung-lo reign-mark within double circle in cobalt blue under the glaze.

Ht. $1\frac{7}{8}''$ Diam. $3\frac{3}{4}''$
Ching-te-chen ware
Probably XVI century

C. 42   Pl. 133b

Conical bowl of paper-thin translucent white porcelain. Straight base. No decoration, but light dots in the paste suggesting 'moons' are visible against light. Covered with thin creamy-white glaze with faint bluish tinge. Bottom of foot-rim unglazed.

Ht. $1\frac{1}{2}''$ Diam. $4\frac{1}{8}''$
Ching-te-chen ware
Ming Dynasty, Yung-lo period

C. 86   Pl. 133c

Deep bowl on small foot, with slightly everted lip. Thin white porcelain. Decorated outside with two dragons in raised slip under transparent white glaze with faint bluish tinge. On the base, Hsüan-te reign-mark within double circle in underglaze cobalt blue. Base of foot-rim unglazed.

Ht. $3\frac{3}{8}''$ Diam. $6\frac{5}{8}''$
Ching-te-chen ware
Early XVIII century

C. 84   Pl. 133d

Wine cup in the shape of a trumpet-mouthed flower (lily?) with two small feet. Creamy-white translucent porcelain covered with a transparent glaze.

Ht. $2\frac{1}{8}''$ Diam. $3\frac{1}{2}''$
Fukien Te-hua ware
Ming Dynasty

C. 39   Pl. 134a

Stem-cup with slightly everted rim and sloping foot. White porcelain. Carved inside and out and on the foot with wide band of peonies and lotus scrolls; formalized lotus petals round lower part of outside of body. In centre the Ch'ien-lung reign-mark within double circle; all delicately engraved in paste under white glaze with faint bluish tint.

Ht. $4''$ Diam. $5\frac{1}{2}''$
Ching-te-chen ware
Ch'ing Dynasty, Ch'ien-lung period

C. 34   Pl. 134b

Bowl with everted, faintly lobed rim. Translucent white porcelain. Outside decorated with five sweeping curved grooves, tapering upwards from quinquefoil scalloped motif encircling the base. Between the curves are shallow cuts swept over with finely incised lines, under a white glaze with faint bluish tinge. In centre the character ya^1 (elegant, refined) in raised slip under the glaze. Bottom of foot-rim unglazed.

Ht. $3''$ Diam. $4\frac{3}{4}''$
Probably XVIII century
Exhib.: Dartington Hall 1949, 115

C. 101   Pl. 134c

Conical bowl with trumpet mouth above bulbous 'body'. White porcelain. Body decorated with freely drawn scroll pattern, lower part of lip with painted leaves, incised under pale blue *ch'ing-pai* type glaze, stained brown at the rim. Bottom of foot-rim unglazed. Two characters *Hsüan-ho* (reign period of Hui-tsung Emperor 1119–25) incised on base under the glaze.

Ht. $1\frac{3}{4}''$ Diam. $3\frac{1}{4}''$
Ching-te-chen ware
XVII or XVIII century

C. 41   Pl. 134d

Deep bowl with everted rim. Thin white porcelain. Decorated inside with two dragons and two *ling-chih* (spirit-fungus); on the base *ling-chih*; outside formalized lotus petals round lower part of body, all carried out in *an-hua* technique under transparent white glaze with faint greenish-blue tint.

Ht. $3\frac{1}{8}''$ Diam. $7\frac{1}{4}''$
Ching-te-chen ware
Ch'ing Dynasty, Yung-cheng period

[1] See p. 157.

15. Miscellaneous Pieces

C. 359 Pl. 135a

Ovoid jar with short neck and slightly everted lip, on concave base. Roughly potted earthenware burnt brown where exposed and covered with a thin, slightly decomposed olive-brown crackled glaze which stops well short of the base in a series of sweeping curves.

Ht. 11″ Diam. $7\frac{3}{4}$″

South China ware. Bought by Lady Barlow in Bali

Sung Dynasty

Export pottery of this type has been widely found in South-East Asia. Probably used for storage on sea voyages

C. 292 Pl. 135b

Ovoid jar with straight neck and everted lip standing on a base which has been subsequently filled in. Hard brown earthenware covered with an uneven greenish-brown glaze through which the decoration has been cut. This consists of two bands round the shoulder, the upper containing roughly-drawn floral scrolls, the lower filled with ten trigram symbols, two of which are repaired. On the body are inscriptions carelessly incised in three large panels separated by scroll borders above a wider scroll band near the base. The inscriptions are only partly decipherable and contain a cyclical date in the series 1393, 1453, 1513, 1573, etc.

Ht. $15\frac{1}{2}$″ Diam. $8\frac{1}{2}$″

South China

Ming Dynasty

C. 394 Pl. 136a

Deep dish of coarse white porcelain, decorated inside with a landscape in the centre,[1] surrounded by seals and little landscape vignettes, rather crudely drawn in underglaze blue and overglaze tomato red. The glazed base has sandy accretions on the foot-rim.

Purchased by Lady Barlow in Bali.

Ht. 3″ Diam. 15″

So-called 'Swatow ware', made for export in kilns in Southern Fukien

Early XVII century

---

[1] This very un-Chinese design may possibly be derived from a copy of a European landscape engraving, such as the little vignette of the town of Middelburg which adorns the frontispiece to the Nijhoff edition of van Lindschoten's *Travels* (1579–92). This type of dish is discussed in my article, 'Chinese Export Porcelain in Singapore: I'. *OA* (N.S.) 3.4 (1957), p. 7.

C. 392   Pl. 136b

Jar with high sharply-cut shoulder, short neck and wide mouth with slightly everted lip, on a bevelled concave base. Four loop-handles on the shoulder. Coarse light buff stoneware covered with a white slip over which is a thin, rich golden-brown glaze unevenly applied and ending in sweeping curves around the foot.

Ht. $10\frac{1}{2}''$ Diam. $10\frac{1}{4}''$

South China, probably made for export

XII–XIV century

16. Annamese and Siamese Stonewares

The four pieces in this group illustrate the influence of Sung celadon on the wares produced in Annam and Siam from the thirteenth to the fifteenth century. The heavily potted stoneware has a glaze of a beautiful greyish-blue colour. Pieces of this kind were widely exported throughout the island empires of South-East Asia, and large numbers have recently been excavated on the island of Luzon in the Philippines.

C. 172 Pl. 137a

Shallow bowl of light grey stoneware, burnt buff where exposed on the unglazed foot and base. Faint suggestion of lotus petals roughly moulded on the outside. Covered with a pale crackled blue-green celadon-type glaze.

Ht. $1\frac{7}{8}''$ Diam. $5\frac{5}{8}''$
Annam
XII–XIV century
A label stuck outside reads 'Village de Ngoc Há près de Hanoi (Tonkin). Emplacement de l'ancienne capitale Dai La Thanh'. This seems quite possible.

C. 371 Pl. 137b

Jar with small mouth and slightly rolled lip, the high shoulder accentuated by double groove cut in the paste. Vertical fluting just perceptible on the side. Stoneware body, covered with finely-crackled grey-green glaze, stopping unevenly on the square-cut foot which is burnt reddish-brown. The base is glazed inside.

Ht. $4\frac{1}{2}''$ Diam. $5\frac{1}{8}''$
Siam, Sawankalok ware
XIV–XV century

C. 385 Pl. 137c

Flattened ovoid jar of heavily-potted light grey stoneware with small mouth and two small loop-handles on the shoulder. Covered inside and out with a crystalline blue-green crackled glaze which stops just short of the slightly concave base. There is no foot.

Ht. $2\frac{3}{4}''$ Diam. $5\frac{1}{4}''$
Either from Annam or from an unidentified kiln in South China
XIV–XV century

C. 328 Pl. 137d

Bowl of buff stoneware, with slightly everted rim, unglazed on the edge. Decorated inside with freely incised floral motif under grey-green celadon glaze; the outside decorated with roughly carved lotus petals. The flat chamfered base is unglazed and burnt light reddish-brown.

Ht. $2\frac{1}{4}''$ Diam. $6\frac{3}{8}''$
Annam
XII or XIII century

17. Korean Wares

When Hsü Ching accompanied the Chinese envoy on a diplomatic mission to Kaesong in 1123, he was particularly struck by the beauty of the celadon being turned out by Korean potters. 'The green pottery is outstanding,' he noted, '. . . it is called *pi-se* (kingfisher blue) by the Koreans; of late the workmanship has greatly improved and colour and glaze are unsurpassed.' At the time of Hsü Ching's visit, Korean potters were still under the influence of Chekiang celadon, and the local flavour shows itself chiefly in an exquisite softness of colour and in an elegant and somewhat mannered drawing by incising in the paste under the glaze. Before the end of the century, however, Korea had made her most notable contribution to the ceramic art of the the Far East, the invention of inlaying in black or white slip under the glaze. The techniques perfected in the twelfth century were continued in the thirteenth, and it is not until the fourteenth century that we find any decline from the superlative quality achieved under the Koryŏ Dynasty.

This collection contains a small but very typical selection of Koryŏ wares, and illustrates four of the techniques used in decorating celadon. There are four pieces with incised decoration, the wine-cup and stand (Pl. 138a) being a particularly lovely piece; one bowl (Pl. 138d) has moulded floral decoration, another (Pl. 140c) a combination of moulding and inlay; while the elaborate wine-cup and stand (Pl. 139a) and the two vases, illustrate the art of inlaying in its heyday and its decline (Pl. 140a). The little oil or cosmetic jar (Pl. 138c) is a beautiful example of the art of painting in black slip under a transparent glaze — a purely Korean refinement on a technique derived from the painted stoneware of North China.

C. 76   Pl. 138a

Cup and stand. The eight-lobed cup is in the form of a lotus flower, each lobe being decorated with delicately incised floral sprays inside and out; the short splayed foot carries three conspicuous spur-marks. The stand has a raised central platform ringed with pendent lotus petals carved in relief and is decorated in the centre with a lotus flower. Around it is a flat band decorated with incised fishes in the water; the raised, eight-lobed horizontal flange has incised floral sprays and is supported on a high splayed eight-lobed foot, each lobe carrying an incised lotus flower. Three spur-marks inside the deep base. Light grey porcellanous ware, covered with a thin blue-green celadon glaze. The cup and stand have been repaired with gold lacquer.

Ht. (total) $3\frac{3}{8}''$ Diam. of stand $5\frac{7}{8}''$
Koryŏ Dynasty, XII century
Cf. National Museum of Korea, Kim and Gompertz, *The Ceramic Art of Korea*, Pl. 26; Eumo., *Cat.* VI, f. 295

C. 79   Pl. 138b

Bowl with slightly everted rim and sharply cut foot. Grey porcellanous stoneware decorated inside with a band of peony leaves round a central formalized flower in the bottom, freely incised in the paste. Covered, except for the foot-rim, with a thin grey-green crazed celadon glaze.

Ht. $2\frac{1}{2}''$　Diam. $6\frac{3}{4}''$
Koryŏ Dynasty, late XI or XII century
Exhib.: OCS 1947 (Celadon), 158

C. 145　Pl. 138c

Globular oil-jar, with short neck, cup-shaped mouth, and low rounded foot. Grey porcellanous stoneware, decorated with leaf sprays around the shoulder, body painted in black under grey-green crazed celadon glaze. Three spur-marks with incrustations on the base.

Ht. $2\frac{1}{8}''$　Diam. $2\frac{1}{4}''$
Koryŏ Dynasty, XIII or early XIV century

C. 255　Pl. 138d

Shallow bowl with slightly everted six-lobed rim and short rounded foot. Grey porcellanous stoneware, decorated inside with a band of flowers and leaves moulded in the paste and covered, except for the foot-rim, with a thin, even grey-green celadon glaze. Three spur-marks on the base.

Ht. $2\frac{5}{8}''$　Diam. $7\frac{1}{2}''$
Koryŏ Dynasty, XI–XII century
Exhib.: OCS 1952 (Ju and Kuan), 29

C. 299　Pl. 139a

Cup and stand. The ten-lobed cup is in the form of a lotus flower, each lobe being decorated with a floral spray, incised on the inside, inlaid between incised borders on the outside; the high splayed foot is scalloped and has three large spur-marks. The stand has a raised central platform ringed with pendent lotus petals carved in relief, with a flower incised in the centre. Around it is a flat band decorated with incised fishes in the water; the raised ten-lobed flange has inlaid floral sprays and is supported on a high ten-lobed splayed foot decorated with incised floral sprays. Inside the deep base are three spur-marks. Buff porcellanous stoneware, covered with a crackled grey-green celadon glaze.

Ht. $4\frac{1}{2}''$　Diam. of stand $5\frac{7}{8}''$
Koryŏ Dynasty, XII–XIII century
Cf. Hyung-pil Chun coll., Kim and Gompertz, op.cit., Pl. 30; Duksoo Palace Museum
　　coll., *Masterpieces of Korean Art*, 1957, 113; H.M. the King of Sweden coll., *Cat.* Pl.
　　85, 1

C. 370　Pl. 139b

Bowl on shallow slightly rounded foot. Grey porcellanous stoneware burnt reddish-brown where exposed on the base. Decorated with two phoenixes swiftly drawn in the paste under a thin, even, grey-green celadon glaze. Mended with gold on the lip.

Ht. $3''$　Diam. $7''$
Koryŏ Period, late XI or XII century

C. 311   Pl. 139c

Bowl with slightly inverted lip on low rounded foot. Greyish-white porcellanous stone-ware decorated inside with two cranes or phoenixes lighly incised in the paste, under a thin, crackled grey-green glaze which completely covers the base. Five spur-marks and adhesions on the base.

Ht. $3\frac{1}{8}''$ Diam. $7\frac{3}{4}''$
Koryŏ Dynasty, late XI or XII century

C. 118   Pl. 140a

Ovoid vase on very shallow foot, with two sides flattened, short neck and rimmed mouth. Grey porcellanous stoneware inlaid on three sides in black and white with birds, flowers and grasses, those on the flat sides being framed in ogival panels. Bands of inlaid over-lapping lotus petals encircle the shoulder and base. Covered with a thin grey-blue celadon glaze, showing some pitting and discoloration on the undecorated side. The base is partly burned red, partly glazed with adhesions of kiln-sand.

Ht. $12\frac{1}{4}''$
Koryŏ Dynasty, late XIII or XIV century
Cf. Jar in Jai-hyung Sohn coll., Kim and Gompertz, op. cit., Pl. 53

C. 135   Pl. 140b

High-shouldered vase (mei-p'ing), with very short neck, small flanged mouth and very low broad foot. Buff porcellanous stoneware, decorated with cranes and clouds inlaid in white clay, the cranes' beaks, crests and legs being black, with a white band of overlapping lotus petals round the base. Covered with a crackled grey-green celadon glaze. The base is glazed, the foot-rim unglazed. A conspicuous crack on one side has been expertly repaired in gold.

Ht. $12\frac{1}{2}''$
Koryŏ Dynasty, late XII or XIII century
Cf. Duksoo Palace Museum coll., Kim and Gompertz, op. cit., Pl. 37

C. 147   Pl. 140c

Bowl, on short rounded foot. Pale buff thinly-potted porcellanous ware decorated inside with four circular medallions containing dragons within a border of leaves and flowers, with a peony in the centre, lightly impressed in the paste. On the outside are four circular medallions each containing a dragon, beneath a narrow scroll border, inlaid in black and white. The bowl is completely covered with a thin, even, crackled grey-green celadon glaze. Three spur-marks on the base.

Ht. $3\frac{1}{4}''$ Diam. $7\frac{1}{2}''$
Koryŏ Dynasty, late XII or XIII century

C. 134   Pl. 140d

Wine-pot, with ten-lobed body, ringed matching lid, plain spout and ringed handle. Grey porcellanous stoneware burnt reddish-brown where exposed on shallow foot. The body is decorated with a delicate flower spray on each lobe, between borders of overlapping lotus petals, inlaid in black and white clay; similar petals adorn the lid. Covered, outside and in, with a crackled olive-green celadon glaze. Three large irregular spur-marks on the base.

Ht. $7\frac{5}{8}''$

Exhib.: OCS 1947 (Celadon)

It is known that good copies of inlaid Koryŏ wares have been made in Japan in recent years. While it is of course impossible to be certain, the heavy potting of this piece compared with other well-known specimens, the thick handle and Western-type spout, all suggest that this may be a recent Japanese imitation.

18. Problem Pieces

We have included in this section a number of pieces which do not seem easily to fit into any of the foregoing groups. They can be roughly classified into five types: 1, early pieces which cannot be precisely placed, such as the beautiful Sung celadon bowl (Pl. 142d); 2, early pieces which have been treated in a peculiar way, possibly at a later date (Pls. 141a and 143c); 3, pieces which belong in a recognized tradition, but which may be of almost any date, such as the lively Tz'u-chou type painted bowl (Pl. 141d); 4, pieces which are here given to a later period than is usual, but which we nevertheless do not consider modern, an example being the striking baluster vase with black and brown glaze (Pl. 143b); 5, and lastly, pieces the authenticity of which is open to question but which we have included for their intrinsic interest, and because decision in these matters can seldom be final.

C. 320   Pl. 141a

Shallow bowl with thickened rim and broad, shallow base. Whitish porcellanous ware covered with flecked greyish-white glaze unevenly finished on the outside. Hobson's description of this piece may be quoted: 'Carved inside on the lapidary's wheel with a ring of rock and wave pattern and four swastika symbols with flowing fillets. . . . T'ang ware, the ornaments added at a subsequent date, the designs being suggested by accidental markings in the glaze.'

Ht. $1\frac{5}{8}''$ Diam. $5\frac{1}{2}''$

The bowl is North China, T'ang; the subsequent decoration late Ming

Publ. Eumo., *Cat.* I, 462

C. 82   Pl. 141b

Ovoid jar with wide mouth, thick lip and very shallow foot. Reddish-brown stoneware covered inside with a greenish-black glaze, outside with an orange-brown glaze which stops short of the base in a straight line.

Ht. $4\frac{3}{8}''$ Diam. $5''$

This jar has been called '? Honan type'. It resembles two pieces in the Hoyt coll., Nos. 322 and 323 in the *Catalogue*, labelled 'Tz'u-chou'. A similar jar in Eumo., *Cat.* II, Pl. LXXV, B. 305 is called 'Yüan'. Brankston reported that he found at Ching-te-chen 'a type with a golden-brown glaze which might easily be confused with Honan or Chihli wares. These are grey, buff or white bodied, and have golden-brown glaze' (*Trans. OCS*, 1938–39, pp. 19–32). The sturdy reddish stoneware body of this piece does not tally with this description. The shape and treatment of the glaze suggest a late, probably Ming, date, and a local ceramic tradition.

C. 47   Pl. 141c

Deep conical bowl with grooved rim, of fine-grained light grey stoneware covered with an olive-brown glaze. There is an unglazed ring in the centre, and the small foot and base are unglazed, revealing the light grey paste. Decorated inside with a band of lotus flowers carved and combed in the paste. Outside are peonies, below a band of formalized floral decoration.

Ht. $4\frac{1}{2}''$ Diam. $8\frac{3}{4}''$

Exhib.: BH 1935, 1339; Manchester 1936, 180; OCS 1947 (Celadon), 89; Arts Council 1953, 56; Musée Cernuschi 1957

This piece has been exhibited as an outstanding example of Sung northern celadon. The smooth, even grey paste and sharply cut foot, the somewhat mechanical incised decoration and dull glaze are not characteristic of the more familiar northern celadons. It resembles the products of the recently discovered Yao-yao kilns in general appearance and in having an unglazed ring in the bottom.

C. 50   Pl. 141d

Bowl with slightly everted rim on straight foot. Hard light buff stoneware covered with a white slip, and decorated with the character *hua*[1] (flower) in the centre, and with leaf sprays in dark brown within broad and narrow bands, and covered with a transparent glaze. Both the glaze and the slip stop well short of the foot. Five spur-marks on the bottom.

Ht. $2\frac{1}{2}''$ Diam. $7''$

Tz'u-chou type

Difficult to date with certainty. May be Sung, or a more recent product of the Tz'u-chou kilns, which have maintained their tradition of free brush painting up to modern times.

C. 198   Pl. 141e

Bowl with thickened rim, on small foot, of grey stoneware covered with a glassy green celadon glaze, with a pronounced crackle stained brown. Decorated inside with a square cusped medallion containing a mythical monster amid plants, carved in the paste, and surrounded with scrolls. Bottom of foot-rim unglazed and burnt brown. Glaze inside base is light yellowish-brown.

Ht. $2\frac{3}{4}''$ Diam. $8\frac{3}{8}''$

This piece, made in the style of Sung northern celadon, has been called 'Chekiang, probably Ming', but its date and place of origin remain a problem.

C. 194   Pl. 142a

Vase (*mei-p'ing*) with short slightly splayed neck, thickened and cut square at the rim. Shallow unglazed foot. Whitish porcellanous ware covered with a thick greyish *kuan*-type crackled glaze, stopping in a straight welt short of the foot. The crackle is stained light red.

Ht. $6\frac{3}{4}''$ Diam. $3\frac{1}{4}''$

Said by the dealer from whom it was purchased to be a Sung excavated piece. However, the heavy potting in two sections luted at the waist, the thick glaze trimmed off sharply short of the base, the somewhat insensitive moulding of the neck and

[1] See p. 157.

mouth, and the pinkish crackle, all suggest a date not earlier than the Ming Dynasty. Probably from Kiangsi.

C. 174   Pl. 142b

Circular bowl with cover. Light buff stoneware covered with a finely-crackled olive-green glaze which has a tendency to flake. The base has a bevelled edge and is unglazed. On the lid the glaze is cut away to form a broken-down character which might be *chi*, 'to offer as a present', or else the family name Ts'ai.[1]

Ht. $2\frac{1}{2}''$ Diam. $4\frac{7}{8}''$

This piece has been exhibited at the Arts Council 1953, 13, as 'Yüeh ware of Shang-lin-hu', but this seems very unlikely. The pinkish stoneware body, and the finely-crackled, uneven glaze which is imperfectly wedded to the body, suggest Hunan, and a T'ang date. Rather less likely, though possible, is that it was made at the T'ang kilns at Ch'iung-lai in Szechwan.

C. 165   Pl. 142c

Wide-mouthed jar with short straight neck, two loop-handles on the shoulder, and broad square-cut roughly finished foot. Light buff stoneware, with white slip, and heavily-crackled whitish glaze stopping well short of the base in an uneven line, but running over it at one point. Touches of brown on the handles.

Ht. $2\frac{3}{8}''$ Diam. $3\frac{1}{4}''$

This piece has been called Tz'u-chou, and is labelled 'Kiangnan Ting ware type' in the Eumo., *Cat.* VI, Pl. XXXV, f. 209. The combination of rough potting, free application of slip and glaze in the T'ang manner, and heavily-crackled *ko* type glaze form an intriguing mixture. It was probably made in North China in the XII or XIII century.

C. 139   Pl. 142d

Bowl with everted lip on small short foot, of grey coarse stoneware. Originally six-lobed. Decorated inside with lotus sprays freely incised in the paste, in the style of Ting ware, under an olive-green crackled glaze. The slightly lobed rim is bound in copper. The bottom of the square-cut foot and the inside of the base are unglazed, showing the paste burnt bluish-grey. An unglazed patch on the side is burnt reddish-buff.

Ht. $2\frac{7}{8}''$ Diam. $7\frac{1}{2}''$

The shape, decoration and technique recall Ting ware, the glaze resembles northern celadon; the dark grey rather coarse paste resembles neither. One authority has called it 'Hangchow celadon', another suggested it might have been made for Borneo, though the quality is unusually fine for an export piece. It is certainly a Sung piece, and probably from Chekiang. Formerly in the le May collection, it may have been acquired in South-East Asia.

Exhib.: Arts Council 1953, 37 ('Northern Celadon')

[1] See p. 157.

PROBLEM PIECES

C. 387 Pl. 143a

Ovoid jar of fine-grained light buff stoneware, with short straight neck and four loop-handles on the shoulder, the body divided horizontally by a sharp ridge. Covered with a very thin light greenish-brown finely-crackled glaze, which stops well short of the slightly splayed flat base in an uneven line. The inside is glazed.

Ht. 7″ Diam. $5\frac{3}{4}$″

This piece resembles the jars found in the celebrated grave of Pu Jen, dated 603, discovered by Dr. Li Chi while excavating at Anyang in the 'thirties. Genuine pieces from this tomb are illustrated in *Sekai Tōji Zenshu* IX, pp. 171, 172, figs. 21 and 25; other genuine pieces of this type illustrated in the same book IX, Pl. 37; and Honey, *Ceramic Art*, Pl. 11(b). If the jar is authentic, the glassy glaze suggests that it may have been refired at a later date.

C. 217 Pl. 143b

Baluster vase with flattened ovoid body and slender trumpet neck rising from a flat shoulder, above a small splayed and moulded pedestal base. Porcelain, covered with a thick golden-brown and brilliant glossy black glaze which stops evenly around the bottom of the foot. Splashes of glaze inside the base. Body made in at least two sections; a join is discerned at the widest point.

Ht. $9\frac{7}{8}$″ Diam. $6\frac{5}{8}$″

These porcelain vases, although in most cases accepted as Sung, seem remote from Sung taste in potting, shape and glaze colour. The shape is a metal rather than a ceramic one. They were probably made at Ching-te-chen, in imitation of Honan black-glazed ware, during the Ming Dynasty.

Exhib.: Dartington Hall 1949 ('Sung'), 104; OCS 1952 (Chün and Brown), 184

Cf. V. & A., Hetherington, *Early Ceramic Wares*, Pl. 41; Eumo., *Cat.* II, Pl. LXIII, B. 258 ('Sung'); Percival David Foundation, No. 302, different shape but same ware ('Ming'); George de Menasce coll., Venice 1954, 498 ('Sung'), also OCS 1960 (Sung), 73; BM, formerly Raphael coll., Hobson, Rackham and King, *Chinese Ceramics in Private Collections*, p. 45, fig. 95 ('Sung')

C. 216 Pl. 143c

Bowl of fine-grained light buff porcellanous ware. Inside divided by thin ridges into six panels, within which are moulded in relief six different flower sprays, with a further spray in the centre. Covered with dark reddish-brown glaze which runs very thin on base and lower part of outside, revealing light buff body.

Ht. $2\frac{3}{8}$″ Diam. $6\frac{3}{4}$″

This bowl has been variously called 'Sung (Ting type)', 'Purple Ting', '*Ying-ch'ing*', and 'modern'. A very similar, but rather smaller, bowl in the Hoyt collection is called Ming (*Cat.* 346). The shape and very light potting suggest that the body of the vessel at least is early, although the decoration suggests the XIII or XIV century. It may have been an unglazed kiln-waster on to which the reddish-brown glaze was fired at a later date.

C. 246   Pl. 143d

Bowl, of almost conical section, of light buff stoneware. Decorated inside with two five-clawed dragons amid clouds beneath a band of squared spirals; in the centre a design of clouds; all moulded in the paste under a pale purple glaze, which has a milky pale bluish tint where it runs thick. The glaze on the outside of the body is thicker, and lightly crackled. Rim and square-cut base unglazed; the latter covered with a purplish-red paint.

Ht. $3\frac{1}{8}''$ Diam. $8\frac{1}{2}''$

Various experts have called this piece 'Yüan', 'Purple Ting', and 'Korean'. It has been suggested that it was first washed over with copper, over which a thin white glaze was applied. The potting is heavy, the drawing poor, the finish rough. It is probably an imitation of purple Ting, not earlier than the XVIII century, and not from Ching-te-chen.

19. Bronzes

In the power of their forms, the compact intensity of their decoration, and the precision of their casting, the ritual bronzes of ancient China must rank as one of the great artistic achievements of early Chinese civilization. The craft itself originated in the Near East at least a thousand years before its appearance in China, but in China it attained a splendour that has no rival in the West. These vessels were cast for the rulers of Shang and Chou, and the feudal aristocracy, for use in sacrifices to their ancestors, to Heaven, or to the cosmic forces. Inscriptions have revealed that occasionally they were also given by the ruler to his wives and daughters as wedding presents. They were not made for burial, though many were eventually interred, and thus came in time to acquire the patina which adds so much to their beauty.

The thirty-odd types of vessel may be classified according to their use in the rites. Vessels for cooking food included the *li* tripod, the *ting* (Pl. 146a), the composite *li-ting* (Pl. 145), and the *hsien* steamer; for offering food on the altar there were the *kuei* (Pl. 152a), *tui*, and *tou*. Among vessels for presenting wine were the *yu* (Pls. 150a & b, 151), *chüeh* (Pl. 147a & b), *kuang, hu, chia, chih* (Pls. 146b and 149b), *tsun* and *ku* (Pl. 148a & b). The shapes may also be considered in terms of their origin. The *li, li-ting, chih, ku* and *tsun*, for example, are clearly derived from neolithic pottery forms (and were in turn imitated in Shang and Chou pottery); the square and rectangular bronzes with all-over zoömorphic decoration, on the other hand, may have originated in vessels of carved wood or bone.

The style of the decoration also derives from several sources. The repeated circles and spirals (*lei-wen*) that form the background to the main décor, and the confining of the ornament on some vessels (e.g. the *chih*, Pl. 152b) to narrow bands, probably originated in the technique of decorating pottery by stamping in the wet clay with a die — a technique long practised in South China. Dr. Li Chi has suggested that the ornate and powerfully conceived animal masks ultimately were derived from the bone and wood carving of China's northern steppe and forest neighbours: their striking resemblance to the wood carving of Siberia and of the north-west coastal Indians of North America has often been remarked.

Chief among the motifs adorning the bronzes is the *t'ao-t'ieh*, an animal mask with attributes of several creatures, which, like the Tibetan 'devil mask', is made deliberately terrifying in order the more effectively to ward off evil and protect its owner. Fine examples of the *t'ao-t'ieh* adorn the *yu* (Pl. 151), and *chih* (Pl. 146b), while a vigorous dissolved *t'ao-t'ieh* forms the main element in the decoration of the *li-ting* (Pl. 145). The *k'uei* dragon (Pls. 150a and 151) takes many forms, but always has a large head with horn or crest, and gaping jaws. The *k'uei*, tiger, snake (Pl. 148a & b) and bird (Pl. 152b) may appear separately, or together make up a *t'ao-t'ieh* mask, while the cicada often occurs on the legs of tripods and on the flaring mouth of the *ku*. The precise significance of these creatures, apart from their obvious protective one, is not known, though there has been much speculation. Excavations at Anyang have revealed that the same motifs were painted on wooden planks and beams, and probably also on matting and leather hangings. This suggests that they formed part of the general repertory of motifs, part magical and protective, part merely decorative, of Shang art.

The simplest and most widely used system for dating the archaic bronzes is that proposed by W. P. Yetts. In this scheme, the bronzes of Shang and early Chou constitute the first phase, those of the middle Chou the second, those of the late Chou or Warring States (Karlgren's Huai style) the third. The discoveries of the last twelve years, however, have greatly complicated the picture. Pre-Anyang bronzes have been discovered at Chengchow; among early Chou vessels it is now possible to distinguish more clearly between survivals from late Shang and new types; the bronzes of the middle centuries of the Chou Dynasty can now be much more securely dated; and it is evident that during the later Chou a number of different styles existed side by side, some preserving archaic elements, others introducing new ones.

This collection contains some notable examples of the bronzes of late Shang and early Chou, several of which are inscribed. Particularly fine are the two *ku*, the two *yu*, the *li-ting* and the covered *chih*; while the restrained silhouette and archaistic decoration of the Warring States style is represented by the handsome flask (Pl. 153a). The three mirrors, all good specimens, include a typical TVL mirror of the middle Han Dynasty, and a rare type of T'ang mirror decorated with dragons in repoussé silver and silver-gilt on lacquer, with mother-of-pearl inlay.

B. 2   Pl. 145

Ritual vessel of the type *li-ting*. Silvery-grey, green and blue patina. A *t'ao-t'ieh* mask, boldly executed against a background of sharply-cut C-scrolls, is centred on each of the three straight tubular legs. The mask has become split up, the body and legs having become detached from one another.[1] A pair of loop-handles rises from the rim.

Inside is an inscription of ten characters in two lines, reading: X *tso Fu Kuei pao tsun i Chi*: 'X made Fu Kuei's precious sacral vessel'.

The last character, which occurs frequently in early bronze inscriptions, has not been positively identified, but it has been suggested that it is *Chi*, according to the *Shu-ching* (Classic of History) the first of the Nine Divisions of China under the legendary Emperor Yü. Here it may be a totem of the X clan.[2]

Ht. (to rim) $7\frac{1}{2}''$

Late Shang Dynasty, XII–XI century B.C.

Publ. W. Watson, *Ancient Chinese Bronzes* Pl. 28a

Cf. Very similar *li-ting publ.* in Karlgren's 'Marginalia to Some Bronze Albums', *BMFEA* 31 (1959), Pl. 41a, taken from Huang Hsün, *Tsun-ku-chai so-chien chi-chin-t'u* (1936), 1.20

---

[1] This type of dissolved *t'ao-t'ieh* is illustrated and discussed by Karlgren, 'Notes on the Grammar of Early Bronze Decor', *BMFEA* 23 (1951), figs. 375, 376, 377, pp. 20–21.

[2] I am indebted for this suggestion, and for assistance in the decipherment of other bronze inscriptions in this section, to the kindness of my colleague Mr. Lee Yim of the School of Oriental and African Studies.

B. 7   Pl. 146a

Ritual vessel of the type *ting*. Green patina with some incrustation. It stands on three outward curving legs. The plain loop-handles rise from the flanged rim. Round the bowl-shaped body is a band of *t'ao-t'ieh*, formed by confronting dragons separated by low, plain vertical flanges, against a background of C-spirals.

Inscribed inside below the rim with a pictograph depicting a *ko*-halberd inside a *ya-hsing*.

The significance of the *ya-hsing* ('of the form of the character *ya*') has long been debated. Recent excavations have confirmed that it was the form made by a type of Shang seal, a number of which have been unearthed at Anyang. It may itself have been a personal name, but more often it appears as a title for a group of court officials. Ch'en Meng-chia believes that the *ya-hsing* 'gradually became the symbol of a special class and [was] often combined with a clan name'.[1] The clan name was sometimes written within the square, as here, sometimes outside it.

Ht. 6⅝″   Diam. of bowl 6″

Shang Dynasty, XIII–XII century B.C.

Cf. Minneapolis Institute of Arts, *publ.* Mizuno, *Bronzes and Jades of Ancient China*, Pl. 20; Nanking Museum, *Ibid.*, Pl. 21

B. 15   Pl. 146b

Ritual vessel of the type *chih*, with cover. Beautifully patinated in green, blue, and red. The body, elliptical in section, has boldly modelled *t'ao-t'ieh* flanked by dragons, below a narrower band of *t'ao-t'ieh* and *k'uei* dragons with heads turned back. The neck has rising cicada blades, while round the high base is a band of snakes. The lid is adorned with two *t'ao-t'ieh*, the conical knob with scrolls.

Inscribed inside the bottom with two characters. The first represents two hands holding an object, and may be an archaic form of *shou*, here used as a name; the second has not been identified.

Ht. 6¾″   Diam. 4¼″

Late Shang Dynasty, XIII–XI century B.C.

B. 3   Pl. 147a

Ritual wine vessel of the type *chüeh*. Green and blue patina, with rather heavy incrustation. The body is encircled by a band of dissolved *t'ao-t'ieh* against a background of squared C-spirals and divided by grooved flanges. Round the lip and on the underside of the spout are stylized cicada forms. The handle springs from the gaping jaws of a bovine head. The projections rising from the lip have caps decorated with whorls. The three legs, triangular in section, are grooved on the two inner faces.

This and the following *chüeh* are said to have been found together at Anyang.

Under the handle is an inscription of two characters. The first has not been identified; the second is probably *Jan*, a name.

[1] Ch'en Meng-chia, quoted by Cheng Te-k'un, 'The *Ya Lü-kuei*', *OA* (N.S.) II, 1 (Spring 1956), 9.

Ht. $7\frac{7}{8}''$ L. $6\frac{7}{8}''$
Late Shang Dynasty, XII–XI century B.C.

B. 4   Pl. 147b

Ritual wine vessel of the type *chüeh*. Green and silvery patina with some incrustation. The body is enclosed by a band of dissolved *t'ao-t'ieh* and squared spirals divided by notched flanges. Round the lip and under the spout are stylized cicada forms. The handle is plain. Short projections rising from the lip have caps decorated with whorls. The legs are plain. On one side of the spout the impression of the cloth in which the vessel was wrapped is clearly visible.[1]

Said to have been found with B. 3 at Anyang.

Under the handle is an ideograph in the form of a dog, *ch'üan*, possibly a clan name.

Ht. $7\frac{3}{4}''$ L. $7''$
Late Shang Dynasty, XII–XI century B.C.

B. 10   Pl. 148a

Ritual vessel of the type *ku*. Green and blue patina. The neck is decorated with 'rising blades' containing dissolved *t'ao-t'ieh* against a background of C-spirals, rising from a band of snakes. The central collar has *t'ao-t'ieh* formed by vertical dissolved dragons separated by high grooved flanges. The flaring base has similar *t'ao-t'ieh* below a band of antithetical dragons.

Ht. $12\frac{3}{4}''$ Diam. of mouth $6\frac{7}{8}''$
Late Shang Dynasty, XI century B.C.

B. 11   Pl. 148b

Ritual vessel of the type *ku*, very similar to B. 10. Red, green and blue patination. The neck has 'rising blades' containing dissolved *t'ao-t'ieh* against a background of C-spirals rising from a narrow band with snakes. The central collar has *t'ao-t'ieh* formed by vertical dissolved dragons separated by grooved flanges; below, a band of antithetical dragons also separated by flanges.

Inscribed inside the base with a pictograph representing a decapitation.

Ht. $12\frac{1}{2}''$ Diam. of mouth $6\frac{1}{8}''$
Late Shang Dynasty, XI century B.C.
Exhib.: OCS 1951 (Bronzes), 39
Cf. Karlgren, *BMFEA* 32 (1960), Type 18a, Pls. 27a, 27b

B. 6   Pl. 149a

Ritual vessel of the type *lei*; may also be classed as a *p'ou*. Silvery blue-green patina, with some incrustation and iron staining. The body is bulbous, the mouth large and lip everted, the high foot pierced in three places. The only decoration consists of two fillets on the neck, a groove round the body, and a slight thickening of the lower part of the foot.

Said to have been excavated at Loyang.

[1] *Cf.* also Vivi Sylwan, 'Silk from the Yin Dynasty', *BMFEA* 9 (1937), 119–26.

Ht. $5\frac{3}{4}''$ Diam. $8\frac{1}{2}''$
Late Shang Dynasty, XII–XI century B.C.

B. 1   Pl. 149b

Ritual vessel of the type *chih*. Smooth green patina with some reddish-brown incrustation. The body is plain except for a band of partially dissolved *t'ao-t'ieh*, forming what
Karlgren has called the 'animal triple band', between thin fillets. There is a double
fillet on the base.

Inside the bottom is an inscription of three characters reading X (clan) *fu ping*
(name of ancestor).

Ht. $5\frac{3}{4}''$ Diam. $2\frac{3}{4}''$
Late Shang Dynasty, XI century B.C.
Cf. chih from 'Tuan Fang altar set', BH 1935, 319 J

B. 9   Pl. 150a

Ritual vessel of the type *yu*, with elliptical body, swing handle and cover. Smooth light
green patina. The body has a narrow band with confronted *k'uei* dragons on either side of a

vestigial flange, above a band of strapwork in low
relief. The swing handle has a diaper pattern on its
upper surface, and terminates at each end in boldly
modelled bovine heads. The cover has a band with confronted *k'uei* dragons and a tubular and slightly everted
knob.

Inside the base is an inscription of nine characters
reading : X X *tso wen-k'ao Fu Ts'ung tsun i*: 'Totem.
X made for Ancestor *Fu Ts'ung* this sacral vessel'.

Inside the cover the two characters *Fu Kuei*, 'Father *Kuei*'.

Ht. $10\frac{1}{4}''$
Early Western Chou Dynasty, late XI–X century B.C.
Exhib.: OCS 1951 (Bronzes), 13
Publ. W. Watson, *Ancient Chinese Bronzes*, Pl. 24b
Cf. Yu in Nelson Gallery, Kansas City, BH 1935, 178 (Ex Tuan
Fang coll.)

B. 12   Pl. 150b

Ritual wine vessel of the type *yu*. Green patina with some incrustation
and evidence of repair. The body is plain except for a band round the neck
composed of dissolved *t'ao-t'ieh* with repeated C-spirals between rows of
circles. Round the base is a narrow band of C-spirals punctuated with bosses
(Karlgren's 'eyed band with diagonals'). The swing-handle has dissolved
k'uei dragons in relief, and terminates at each end with the beautifully modelled head of a horned animal. The cover has a broad band repeating the
main decoration of the body, and a short everted tubular knob.

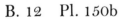

Inscribed inside the cover. The first character, depicting a kneeling figure with hand raised, is borrowed as a clan or tribal name; the second may be equivalent to *hsing* (fortunate, prosperous, but here concerned with offering); the third and fourth read *Fu Hsin*, a name, presumably that of the ancestor to whom the vessel was dedicated.

The same inscription, read laterally, appears on the bottom of the vessel.

Ht. to top of knob $9\frac{1}{4}''$ Diam. $5''$

Early Western Chou Dynasty, late XI–X century B.C.

Cf. Inscribed *yu* in van der Mandele coll., BH 1935, 196 and *Commem. Cat.* Pl. 14; similar but with rope-handle in Palmer coll., OCS 1951 (Bronzes), 28; Karlgren's 'B style', Type 27, *BMFEA* 32, Pl. 41a; Minneapolis Institute of Arts, *publ.* Mizuno, *Bronzes and Jades of Ancient China* (Tokyo, 1960), Pl. 89

B. 8   Pl. 151

Ritual vessel of the type *yu*. Grey-green and blackish patina; the lid, which has become fixed to the body, is more heavily corroded. The main decoration consists of boldly modelled *t'ao-t'ieh* flanked by vertical dragons. Around the rim, pairs of *k'uei* dragons confront a horned mask in higher relief, while round the base pairs of *k'uei* dragons confront a dissolved *t'ao-t'ieh* mask. The top of the lid has back-to-back *t'ao-t'ieh* above a band of *k'uei* dragons. Diagonal *k'uei* dragons adorn the handle. The underside of the base has back-to-back *t'ao-t'ieh*, echoing those on the lid, modelled in raised fillet relief.

Ht. to top of knob $8\frac{7}{8}''$ Diam. $7''$

Late Shang or Early Chou Dynasty, XI century B.C.

Publ. by Karlgren, 'Marginalia on Some Bronze Albums', *BMFEA* 31 (1959), Pl. 32a; Karlgren discusses this large category of *yu* on p. 307

B. 14   Pl. 152a

Ritual vessel of the type *kuei*. Patchy green patina. The body is decorated, between two raised fillets, with dissolved *t'ao-t'ieh* masks and dissolved vertical dragons, with a small horned animal mask in higher relief at the centre of each side. The base has pairs of *k'uei* dragons confronting each other on either side of what Karlgren called the 'hooked forehead shield', an abbreviated and shrunken form of *t'ao-t'ieh*. The handles spring from bovine heads; hooked lugs hang from the underside.

Ht. $5\frac{1}{8}''$ Diam. of bowl $7\frac{1}{2}''$

Early Western Chou Dynasty, late XI–X century B.C.

B. 13   Pl. 152b

Ritual vessel of the type *chih*. Dark greenish patination, which has been rubbed down, indicating it has probably been in a collection in China. Plain except for a band round the neck containing long-tailed birds confronting bovine masks. The foot is damaged.

Ht. $6\frac{1}{2}''$ Diam. $7''$

Early Western Chou Dynasty, X century B.C.

Cf. Seligman coll., *publ.* Hansford, *The Seligman Collection*, Pl. VI, A. 7

B. 16   Pl. 153a

Ritual vessel of the type *pien-hu*. Smooth silvery grey-green patina with some reddish patches. The body is flask-shaped, with two flat sides, short tubular neck and rectangular base. *T'ao-t'ieh* masks with loose ring handles are applied to the shoulders.

Ht. $9\frac{7}{8}''$ W. $10\frac{1}{4}''$ Diam. $4\frac{1}{4}''$

Late Warring States, IV–III century B.C.

Cf. Malmö Museum coll., Venice 1954, 125; *pien-hu* with 'teeming hooks' and bands imitating pelt and leather strapping in coll. of Chinese Government, *publ. Chung-hua wen-wu chi-ch'eng*, 1954, Vol. I, Pl. 55; similar to the above but inlaid with gold, formerly J. Pilster coll., Berlin, *publ.* Sullivan, *An Introduction to Chinese Art*, Pl. 19; a fine early Han specimen unearthed in 1957 from a tomb at Ch'ing-chen in Kweichow, *publ. K'ao-ku hsüeh pao*, 1959, 1, p. 94

B. 5   Pl. 153b

Ritual wine ladle of the type *shao*. The handle is a recent restoration.

L. $9\frac{1}{4}''$

Early Western Chou Dynasty, X–IX century B.C.

Exhib.: OCS 1951 (Bronzes), 71

Cf. Stoclet coll., BH 1935, 237; 'Pao-chi altar set', Chinese Government coll., BH 1935, 319 L; von Lochow coll., Venice 1954, 40

B. 17   Pl. 154a

Bronze mirror of TLV type.[1] Silvery metal with green patination. The knob is surrounded by nine studs, the spaces at the corners of the square being occupied by the four characters *ch'ang i tzu sun* 'May you forever have sons and grandsons', a very common inscription on Han mirrors.[2] The main zone, with its eight bosses, TLV elements and eight animals in fillet relief denoting the points of the compass, follows the familiar pattern of mirrors of this type. Beyond lies a band of hatching, and on the thicker rim a saw-tooth pattern and a band of dissolved animal scrolls within a plain outer border.

Diam. $5\frac{1}{2}''$

Han Dynasty, *c.* 100 B.C.–A.D. 100

Cf. Mirror in H.M. the King of Sweden's coll., *Cat.* Pl. 36,5

B. 19   Pl. 154b

Bronze mirror, with eight lobes in the form of lotus petals, in each of which is a flower, or butterfly and flower. The central zone represents the moon, and is decorated with lunar symbols in cast relief. The boss is in the form of a tortoise, symbol of long life and of the *yin*

---

[1] The cosmological significance of this design is discussed in detail by Schuyler Cammann in his 'The "TLV" Pattern on Cosmic Mirrors of the Han Dynasty', *Journal of the American Oriental Society*, Vol. 68 (1948), 159–67. See also L. S. Yang, 'A Note on the So-called TLV Mirrors and the Game Liu-po', *Harvard Journal of Asiatic Studies*, Vol. IX (1947), 3/4, 202–6, and 'An Additional Note on the Ancient Game Liu-po', *Ibid.*, Vol. XV (1952), 1/2, 124–39.

[2] See B. Karlgren, 'Early Chinese Mirror Inscriptions', *BMFEA* 6 (1934), p. 16, inscription no. 3.

(female) element. To the left is the toad pounding the elixir of immortality, above it the fairy Ch'ang O bearing a tablet with the characters *ta chi* (great fortune); to the right, the toad is leaping up towards its cassia tree from a pool labelled *shui* (water), also a *yin* element. Formalized clouds complete the design. A high proportion of tin gives the bronze a silvery colour, and there is some green oxidization. Traces of the silk in which the mirror was wrapped in the tomb are visible on both sides.

Diam. $7\frac{1}{2}''$ Thickness $\frac{3}{8}''$

T'ang Dynasty

Cf. Rubbing of what appears to be an identical mirror, *publ.* in Shen Tsung-wen, *T'ang Sung t'ung ching* (Bronze Mirrors of T'ang and Sung), Peking, 1958, supp. fig. 49. No particulars are given

B. 18   Pl. 154c

Bronze mirror decorated on the back with silver, silver-gilt, and mother-of-pearl inlaid in lacquer. The central boss is encircled with twelve discs of mother-of-pearl, four of which are missing. The main zone is decorated with two elaborate scaled dragons in repoussé silver and silver-gilt, set in a field of lacquer laid on coarse hemp cloth. The rim is inlaid with a band of peony flowers and leaves of carved and engraved mother-of-pearl. Much of the surface lacquer is missing, what remains is black but may originally have been dark blue. The mirror has been damaged through burial. The tassel is modern.

T'ang mirrors decorated with mother-of-pearl inlay are not uncommon, but the combination of this technique with repoussé silver and silver-gilt is very rare.

Diam. $8\frac{7}{8}''$

T'ang Dynasty

Exhib.: OCS 1960 (T'ang), 240

Cf. T'ang mirror in BM, decorated with twin phoenixes in silver inlaid with mother-of-pearl; T'ang mirror with phoenixes, *gandharvas* and flowers inlaid in gold and silver, in coll. of Shanghai Cultural Preservation Committee, *illus.* in colour in *Wen-wu* 1957.8, opposite p. 8; eight-lobed mirror with birds and flowers inlaid in gold and silver, in the Shōsōin Repository, Nara, detail *illus.* in Ishida and Wada, The *Shōsōin*, Tokyo, 1954, Pl. 27; bronze mirror, also in the Shōsōin, with similar dragons in relief, but with necks entwined, *Ibid.*, Pl. 26; eight mirrors with mother-of-pearl inlay, *illus.* in *T'ang Sung t'ung ching* (Bronze Mirrors of T'ang and Sung), Peking, 1958, Pls. 50–57; Bo Gyllensvärd, *T'ang Gold and Silver*, Stockholm, 1957, fig. 56

20. Jades

Every Chinese scholar and antiquarian would include in his collection at least a few pieces of jade, as ornaments for his desk, to dangle from his girdle, or to keep in his pocket and fondle from time to time, enjoying at the same time the delight of the stone to sight and touch, and the traditional moral virtues attributed to it. This collection is similarly enriched by a group of jades which, though few in number, well illustrate the beauty of the material, the techniques of cutting, and the variety of traditional forms in which it was carved. These aspects of the lore of jade have been fully explored by Western writers, and through their work the Western connoisseur can appreciate something of the significance accorded in China to this beautiful material.

The sources of the jade used by the Chinese lapidary have long been a problem to experts. It was well known that Khotanese nephrite had been used at least since the Han Dynasty, while Burmese jadeite became popular in China in more recent times. No source of jade stone was ever found in China, and Western authorities came to the conclusion, as Hansford put it, that 'the belief, that deposits of jade stone existed at places in China Proper, rests on no foundation of ascertained fact, but may be accounted for by loose terminology and false identification of other stones with nephrite'.[1]

However, new light has recently been thrown on the question from two sources. The Swedish geologist Arno Schüller reports that snow-white jade with green flecks, of a type which he found in the market in Hangchow, and later in Peking, is identified with a type of jade stone reported by H. C. Lee in 1936 as being found in a small hill, Tu-shan, about three miles north-east of Nanyang in southern Honan.[2] This is of particular interest as it throws light on the statement of the fifth-century Chinese writer T'ao Hung-ching, quoted in the Ming pharmacopoea *Pen-ts'ao kang-mu*, that in his time good white jade came from Nanyang. To this important discovery we may add the recent word of a noted Peking jade-carver, who states that among the newly discovered native hardstones at the disposal of the Chinese lapidary is a dark green jade from Honan.[3]

There remains, however, the problem of dating. Hitherto, a number of convenient rule-of-thumb criteria have been available, and are still generally employed in sale and exhibition catalogues. No jades were allotted to the Six Dynasties, very few to T'ang or Ming; beautifully carved and elaborate pieces were Ch'ien-lung, faithful copies of the antique, Sung; ugly or fussy pieces nineteenth century. Recumbent buffaloes used to be Han and are now Ming. This is clearly unsatisfactory, and yet it reflects the problem posed by the lack of datable jades from China. Twelve years ago, the jades from the tenth-century tomb of the Emperor Wang Chien, opened at Chengtu in 1942–43, were the only post-Warring States specimens to have been scientifically excavated.

---

[1] S. H. Hansford, *Chinese Jade Carving* (1950), 55.

[2] Arno Schüller, 'Shichangit, ein Epi-Metaleukophyr-Pyroxenit (Plagioklas-Hornblende-Jadeitit) als Randfazies ehemaliger leukophyrischer Gänge in Serpentin und Gabbro', *Bull. of the Geological Institutions of the University of Uppsala* XL (June 1961), 429–53.

[3] Pan Ping-heng, 'Chinese Jade Carving', *China Reconstructs*, November 1959, p. 17.

The strenuous archaeological activity of the past twelve years, however, has begun to fill out the picture, as the following list of more important excavations may indicate :

1. Han tombs in Loyang. Ritual objects.[1]
2. Western Han tombs in Canton.[2] Finds include *huan*, *pi*, fishes, pendant, and a scabbard-fitting very similar to Pl. 157c.
3. Third-century tomb near Nanking.[3] This tomb contained, in addition to early Yüeh ware chicken-ewers very similar to Pl. 69b, a jade *ts'ung* of simple archaic shape, two soapstone *pi*, and soapstone plaques which were evidently cheap substitutes for jade. The *ts'ung*, seen by itself, would certainly have been ascribed to the Chou Dynasty. Whether at the time of burial it was an ancient piece, or whether it was a 'modern' imitation, it is impossible to tell. Its discovery in a tomb of the Eastern Chin suggests that accurate replicas of archaic ritual jades were being made at a very early date : indeed, there may have been no period when they were *not* made.
4. Sui tomb at Sian, Kuo-chia-t'an, with jade plaques, pendants and other objects, and coins dated 581.[4]
5. Sui tomb at Sian dated 610 with jade plaques.[5]
6. T'ang tomb at Chengtu.[6] No date, but after 850. Contained a jade seal, miniature *tsun* vase, belt with eight square plaques and a tail, pendants, etc. The seal and belt are not unlike those from the Wang Chien tomb.
7. T'ang tomb at Sian which yielded seven jade belt plaques (with a silver buckle), now in the collection of Ch'en Jen-t'ao, Hongkong. Opened privately before 1950.[7]
8. Tomb of Wang Chien, Chengtu (dated 918). Eulogistic jade book, seal and belt.[8]
9. Two tombs of princes of Southern T'ang at Nanking.[9] That of Li Pien (943) contained twenty-three engraved jade tablets, similar to the Wang Chien jade book. The jades were of poorer quality than those in the Wang Chien tomb.
10. Ming tomb at Chengtu[10] containing a jade two-eared cup.
11. Tomb of Wan-li Emperor near Peking (dated 1620).[11] Spectacular jade vessels and jewellery.
12. Tombs of concubines of Wan-li and T'ien-ch'i, in suburbs of Peking. Jade objects and jewellery.[12]

While this brief list shows a considerable advance on the position in 1949, it is still too meagre an inventory to enable us to establish any clear dating, except perhaps in regard to

[1] *Lo-yang Sha-kuo Han-mu* (Peking, 1959).
[2] *K'ao-ku hsüeh-pao* 1958.2, p. 72 and Pl. 15.
[3] *Wen-wu* 1956.6, figs. 17, 18, 21, 22.
[4] *Wen-wu* 1957.8.
[5] *Wen-wu* 1957.8; 1959.8.
[6] *Wen-wu* 1957.5.
[7] *Publ.* by Cheng Te-k'un, 'T'ang and Ming Jades', *Trans. OCS*, Vol. 28, 1953–54, 1–13.
[8] M. Sullivan, 'The Excavation of the Royal Tomb of Wang Chien', *Trans. OCS*, Vol. 23, 1947–48, 17–26.
[9] *Report on the Excavation of Two T'ang Mausoleums* (Peking 1957).
[10] *Wen-wu* 1956.10, p. 47.
[11] Brief illustrated report in *China Reconstructs*, March 1959.
[12] See Hsia Nai, 'New Archaeological Discoveries', *China Reconstructs*, July–August 1952.

the jade belt and eulogistic book of which several T'ang and tenth-century examples have been excavated. The problem of distinguishing between, say, a Sung copy of an archaic piece and a Ch'ing one, still remains. Faced with this difficulty in selecting jades for the Arts of the Sung Dynasty Exhibition organized by the Oriental Ceramic Society in 1960, the Committee concluded that archaic motifs were more congenially interpreted and freely drawn under the Sung, and that by contrast Ch'ing archaisms tend to be more formal and decorative, 'the original understanding of the style-language having been almost forgotten.' This seems a reasonable assumption, and has the virtue of proposing some kind of basis, however tentative, for stylistic analysis. But what do we know of Sung archaisms? At the time of writing, no important excavations of Sung jades have been published. The evidence of Sung porcelain, moreover, would suggest that archaic forms were by no means always reproduced faithfully. A great deal of minute analysis will have to be carried out on the decoration of jades and related material such as porcelain, lacquer and metalwork, before such stylistic criteria can safely be applied to the dating of jade; and even then, so adept is the lapidary at copying, that all that could be said in most cases would be that a piece was 'Sung or later', 'Ming or later', and so on. To give but one example of the pitfalls that awaits us, the handsome *kuei* (Pl. 159a) has three times been published as a Sung piece, presumably because it faithfully reproduces an archaic bronze vessel, and this is now taken by Western authorities as a Sung characteristic. On the other hand, the criterion adopted for the Sung exhibition would probably assign the covered *fang-ting* (Pl. 160a) to the Ch'ing Dynasty because of its playful and inaccurate assemblage of archaic motifs. It does indeed seem likely that the latter is a late piece: it bears all the hall-marks of eighteenth-century taste. But can we be so sure that the *kuei* is Sung? Might it not have been copied from a genuine archaic bronze in the Ch'ien-lung period? — or indeed, at any time in the last thousand years? The condition of the jade, again, may not give us any clues. A Ming piece which has been buried, for example, would probably be more heavily corroded than a Sung piece which has not.

Although the foregoing comments should be enough to indicate how hazardous it is to attribute dates to individual jades on stylistic grounds alone, I have ventured one or two suggestions in the following notes, feeling that it is more satisfactory, both to writer and reader, to make a guess than simply to leave a question-mark.

J. 16   Pl. 155a

Disc of greyish-white jade, tinged on the outer edges with brown and black. The decoration on each side is divided into two zones, separated by a raised fillet. The inner zone contains regular rows of studs, the so-called grain-pattern, but lacking the incised spiral. The outer zone contains a band of animals carved in relief; three are dragons, the fourth a tiger, while at one point a phoenix head appears among the tail-scrolls. The design on the reverse is similar, but not identical. Projecting from the outer rim is a winged lion supported by cloud-scrolls.

Diam. $6\frac{1}{2}''$ Thickness $\frac{3}{8}''$

Either a Han piece, or a very close imitation of the Han style. A clue to the date is the rock and plant motif which separates the confronting dragon and tiger on one side. These elements may be found on mirrors and inlaid and engraved bronzes of the

151

Han period and are not likely to have been so convincingly reproduced if this were a later work in the Han style. This combined with the rugged assurance of the carving suggest that this is a Han piece.

Exhib.: Venice 1954, 221

J. 5   Pl. 155b

Plaque in the shape of a stylized bird with its head turned back over its shoulder. White jade, that with time and handling has turned the colour of old ivory. The body is decorated in archaic style with studs and C-scrolls. The carving is approximately the same on both sides.

Ht. $1\frac{3}{4}''$ L. $3''$ Thickness $\frac{1}{4}''$

T'ang or Sung Dynasty

Exhib.: OCS 1948 (Jade), 90 ('T'ang, dragon'); OCS 1960 (Sung), 248

Cf. This beautiful piece has some stylistic affinity with the plaque formerly in the Bruce coll., *illus.* Hansford, *Chinese Jade Carving*, Pl. XXVa ('T'ang'), also in OCS 1948 (Jade), 97 ('T'ang')

J. 14   Pl. 156a

Perforated belt-ring (*tai-huan*) made to engage with a belt-hook. Green jade flecked with brown, and showing some corrosion and encrustation resulting from burial. The plaque is in the form of a shield the upper part of which terminates in a simplified monster mask. An oval ring on one side contains engraved cloud-scrolls; the other side has open scrolls, two of which end in bird's heads. The 'shield' is supported on one side by a dragon, on the other by a vestigial phoenix and clouds. The back is similarly carved, except that there is a rope pattern round the central hole.

L. $4\frac{5}{8}''$ Diam. $4\frac{5}{8}''$ Diam. of hole $2''$

Han Dynasty

Cf. Hansford, *Chinese Jade Carving*, Pl. XXIIIc & d Hansford coll., ('Han or earlier'); a similar shaped plaque, called a *p'ei*, excavated in a Western Han tomb near Canton, in 1957, is reproduced in *Wen-wu* 1958.5, p. 75

J. 6   Pl. 156b

Disc of *pi* type. Pearly grey jade shading to brown on one side. The obverse is decorated with orderly rows of raised knobs, the reverse with elongated C-spirals in low relief. The central hole is almost filled with the figure of a crouching, high shouldered protective demon whose body is covered with scales. On the upper edge are two feline creatures back to back, their tails entwined, their heads turned back over their shoulders. On the lower rim are two crouching animals (dogs?), back to back with conjoined tails. Probably a mortuary piece.

Diam. $2\frac{3}{4}''$ L. $3\frac{3}{8}''$ Thickness $\frac{1}{4}''$

T'ang Dynasty

Exhib.: OCS 1960 (Sung), 247

J. 10   Pl. 157a

Water-vessel in the form of a winged feline monster with head turned back over its right shoulder. Greenish-white jade with slate-grey markings. The body is hollow and there is a circular hole in the middle of its back. The head, wings and feet are vigorously modelled, details of pinions and fur being engraved. A pair of horns, now broken off, once rose from above the ears and suggest that this might be a dragon.

This piece could be as early as the Six Dynasties. It is rather similar in style to a beautiful winged beast in the Palace Museum collection, traditionally labelled Han, though the editors of *Chinese Art Treasures*, the catalogue of the exhibition touring the United States in 1961–62, write of this object (No. 132), 'the stylistic resemblance to the famous beasts at the Liang imperial tombs near Nanking is too striking to be overlooked; and although this is not positive evidence for dating the jade beast as late as the stone lions, e.g. in the VI century A.D., it does suggest that it might be later than Han.'

L. $4\frac{5}{8}''$ Ht. $2\frac{3}{8}''$ W. $2\frac{1}{2}''$

Exhib.: OCS 1948 (Jade), 119 ('Feline Monster, Sung or Ming'); OCS 1960 (Sung), 246 ('Winged lion')

J. 11   Pl. 157b

Two puppies playing together. Light green jade with patches of reddish-brown.

L. $4\frac{7}{8}''$

T'ang Dynasty

Exhib.: OCS 1948 (Jade), 122

J. 3   Pl. 157c

Scabbard-fitting in light greyish jade tinged with brown. The upper surface is decorated with a pattern of interrelated C-scrolls, terminating at the bottom in the eyes and bushy eyebrows of a monster mask.

L. $3\frac{3}{8}''$ W. $1''$ Thickness $\frac{5}{8}''$

Late Warring States or early Han

Cf. Many scabbard fittings of this type are known; Desmond Gure coll., Venice 1954, 206; a similar specimen in glass in the coll. of H.M. the King of Sweden, *Cat.* Pl. 55, No. 2

J. 9   Pl. 158a

Disc of *pi* type; grey-green jade, partly stained with brown. The obverse bears a sinuous winged dragon with bushy tail confronting a flaming pearl, carved in very high relief. The reverse is decorated in two zones with carving in very low relief, separated by a band of rope pattern. The inner zone has a ring of C-scrolls within a ring of bosses; the outer zone has eight roundels each containing a pair of C-scrolls and bosses.

Diam. $4''$ Thickness $\frac{3}{8}''$

Difficult to date, but unlikely to be earlier than Sung

J. 7   Pl. 158b

Belt-hook (*tai-kou*) carved in the form of a phoenix with its head turned back. Ivory-white jade shading in places to black. The head is finely carved, the feathers engraved. The underside of the knob is decorated with a floral pattern.

L. $4\frac{5}{8}''$

Ch'ing Dynasty

J. 4   Pl. 158c

Disc of *pi* type, of greyish-white jade, shading to bluish-black on one side. One face is decorated with a formalized, sinuous tiger in low, flat relief. The carving is rather crude, the surface pitted; the outer edges are much worn, suggesting that this is an early piece which has had long use as a pendant or dress ornament.

Diam. $2\frac{7}{8}''$ Thickness $\frac{3}{8}''$

Sung Dynasty or possibly earlier

J. 15   Pl. 159a

Vessel in the form of a sacrificial bronze of the type *kuei* of the Second Phase, or middle Chou, *c.* IX–VIII century B.C. Greenish-grey jade with some lighter and darker markings. The body is decorated with vertical ribbings; below the neck is a concave zone containing archaistic dragons carved in very low relief between vertical flanges, on either side of a tiger mask. The foot is similarly decorated with *k'uei* dragons separated by vertical flanges. The handles spring from the gaping jaws of vigorously modelled tigers, and return to the body in a plain curve, from which hangs a notched lug. The base and interior are plain. One of the handles has been broken and the tiger mask restored. The restoration is not modern.

H. $3\frac{3}{4}''$ Diam. $6\frac{5}{8}''$ Diam. of bowl $4''$

Sung Dynasty or later

Exhib.: OCS 1948 (Jade), 109 ('Sung'); OCS 1960 (Sung), 245

Publ. S. H. Hansford, *Chinese Jade Carving*, Pl. XXVIIa, 'Sung'

J. 12   Pl. 159b

Water buffalo lying down, with his head turned back to look at a horned, scaly creature with a bushy tail who is crawling up over his rump. A rope, indicated in shallow relief, passes through the buffalo's nose and over his back. Powerfully and simply modelled in olive-green jade shading in parts to brown and black.

Ht. $2''$ L. $4\frac{1}{8}''$

Possibly Ming Dynasty

Cf. The celebrated jade buffalo formerly in Raphael coll. now in Fitzwilliam Museum, Cambridge, *illus.* in BH 1935, *Comm. Cat.* Pl. 49, No. 480, there labelled 'perhaps Han'

J. 17   Pl. 160a

Sacrificial vessel in the form of a *fang* (i.e. square) *ting* on four legs with cover. Ivory-white jade with some fine crazing and a little surface discoloration. The rectangular body is adorned on all four sides with fanciful masks in ribbon relief based on the *t'ao-t'ieh*, divided by vertical serrated flanges decorated with an engraved diaper. The legs and outward-curving handles are plain. The *t'ao-t'ieh* separated by flanges are repeated on the sloping sides of the lid, whose raised hollow knob is decorated with an engraved key pattern above toothed flanges.

Ht. $6\frac{3}{8}''$ W. $7\frac{1}{4}''$

This fine piece has probably been buried, but stylistically is hardly likely to be earlier than the XVII century

J. 13   Pl. 160b

Sleeve-weight (?) in the form of a sitting phoenix with its head turned slightly to the right. Light grey-green jade with some brown discoloration and patches of deep surface corrosion. The neck and back are decorated with a scale pattern in low relief derived from middle Chou bronze décor, the wings and outer tail-feathers with squared scrolls, the centre of the tail with C-scrolls. A band of C-scrolls passes round the chest, and open in-turned square scrolls in sharp relief fill the space between the wings and the flat stand on which the phoenix rests.

Ht. $3\frac{1}{8}''$ L. $5\frac{3}{8}''$

In spite of the corrosion, this piece seems from the stylistic point of view unlikely to be earlier than the XVII century

Chinese Characters Referred to in the Text

C. 17	文 位 南 樓	C. 157	壽 山 福 海
C. 32	娛 軒	C. 174	齋 蔡
C. 34	雅	C. 176	祐 年 五 月 初
C. 50	花	C. 183	酒 氣 沖 天
C. 54	石 林　石 山 二	C. 249	日
C. 55	高	C. 258	李 右　蒼　汪
C. 69	福	C. 281	楊
C. 90	錢	C. 284	王
C. 97	吳 明 之	C. 285	合
C. 108	福 祿	C. 330	王 園 音

Cross References

Barlow Catalogue Numbers to Plate Numbers

CROSS REFERENCES

CROSS REFERENCES

CROSS REFERENCES

C. 379	Pl. 66c	B.	2	Pl. 145	B.	19	Pl. 154b
C. 380	Pl. 75b	B.	3	Pl. 147a			
C. 381	Pl. 22a	B.	4	Pl. 147b	J.	3	Pl. 157c
C. 382	Pl. 23a	B.	5	Pl. 153b	J.	4	Pl. 158c
C. 383	Pl. 131b	B.	6	Pl. 149a	J.	5	Pl. 155b
C. 384	Pl. 51a	B.	7	Pl. 146a	J.	6	Pl. 156b
C. 385	Pl. 137c	B.	8	Pl. 151	J.	7	Pl. 158b
C. 386	Pl. 67a	B.	9	Pl. 150a	J.	9	Pl. 158a
C. 387	Pl. 143a	B.	10	Pl. 148a	J.	10	Pl. 157a
C. 388	Pl. 32a	B.	11	Pl. 148b	J.	11	Pl. 157b
C. 389	Pl. 61b	B.	12	Pl. 150b	J.	12	Pl. 159b
C. 390	Pl. 25c	B.	13	Pl. 152b	J.	13	Pl. 160b
C. 392	Pl. 136b	B.	14	Pl. 152a	J.	14	Pl. 156a
C. 393	Pl. 103a	B.	15	Pl. 146b	J.	15	Pl. 159a
C. 394	Pl. 136a	B.	16	Pl. 153a	J.	16	Pl. 155a
		B.	17	Pl. 154a	J.	17	Pl. 160b
B. 1	Pl. 149b	B.	18	Pl. 154c			

Abbreviations Used in the Text and Bibliography

BH	Burlington House, International Exhibition of Chinese Art
BM	British Museum
BMFEA	*Bulletin of the Museum of Far Eastern Antiquities* (Stockholm)
Cat.	*Catalogue*
Eumo.	(George) Eumorfopoulos
Exhib.	*Exhibited*
FECB	*Far Eastern Ceramic Bulletin*
Illus.	*Illustrated*
MEA	Museum of Eastern Art (Oxford)
OA	*Oriental Art*
OA (N.S.)	*Oriental Art* (New Series)
OCS	Oriental Ceramic Society
Publ.	*Published*
ROM	Royal Ontario Museum (Toronto)
Trans.	*Transactions*
V. & A.	Victoria and Albert Museum

Bibliography

Aga-Oglu, K., 'The Relationship between the Ying-ch'ing, Shu-fu and Early Blue and White'. *FECB* 8, December 1949.

Arts Council, London, *Chinese Ceramics from Sir Alan Barlow's Collection*. London, 1953.

Arts Council, London, *The National Art Treasures of Korea*. London, 1961.

Barlow, J. A. N., C.B., C.B.E., 'The Collector and the Expert'. *Trans. OCS* 1936–37, pp. 87–102.

Bluett, Edgar E., *Chinese Pottery and Porcelain in the Collection of Mr. and Mrs. Alfred Clark*. Reprinted from *Apollo* (n.d.).

Boston Museum of Fine Arts, *The Charles B. Hoyt Collection*. Boston, 1952.

Brankston, A. D., 'An Excursion to Ching-te-chen and Chi-an-fu in Kiangsi'. *Trans. OCS* 1938–39, pp. 19–32.

Brankston, A. D., *Early Ming Wares of Ching-te-chen*. Peking, 1938.

Chekiang Provincial Committee for the Administration of Cultural Properties, 'Te-ch'ing yao tz'u-ch'i' (Pottery of the Te-ch'ing Kilns). *Wen-wu* 1959.12, pp. 51–52.

Chekiang Provincial Committee . . . , 'Che-chiang Huang-yen ku-tai ch'ing-tz'u yao-chih t'iao-ch'a chi' (Study of the Celadon Ware Kilnsites of Huang-yen in Chekiang). *K'ao-ku t'ung-hsün* 8, pp. 44–47.

Chekiang Provincial Committee . . . , 'Huang-yen Hsiu-ling shui-k'u ku mu fa-chüeh pao-kao' (Report of Ancient Tombs Excavated at the Hsiu-ling Dam, Huang-yen). *K'ao-ku hsüeh-pao* 1958.1, pp. 111–30.

Ch'en Wan-li, *Chung-kuo Ch'ing-tz'u Shih-lüeh* (Outline History of Chinese Celadon). Shanghai, 1956.

Ch'en Wan-li, 'Hsing, Yüeh erh yao chi Ting yao' (Concerning the Two Wares of Hsing and Yüeh and Ting Ware). *Wen-wu* 1953.9.

Ch'en Wan-li, *Sung-tai Pei-fang Min-chien Tz'u-ch'i* (Northern People's Ceramics of the Sung Dynasty). Peking, 1955.

Ch'en Wan-li, 'T'iao-ch'a Min-nan ku-tai yao-chih hsiao-chi' (Brief Notes on Reported Ancient Kilnsites in Southern Fukien). *Wen-wu* 1959.9, pp. 56–59.

Ch'en Wan-li, *Yüeh Ch'i T'u-lu* (Illustrations of Yüeh Ware). Shanghai, 1937.

Cheng Te-k'un, 'The Ya Lü-kuei'. *OA* (N.S.) II.1 (Spring 1956) pp. 3–10.

Chiang Hsüan-i, *Chi-chou Yao* (Chi-chou Ware). Peking, 1958.

Chiang Ssu-ch'ing, 'Kuan-yü T'ang-tai Hung-chou-yao wen-t'i' (Concerning the Problem of T'ang Hung-chou Ware). *Wen-wu ts'an-k'ao ts'e-liao* 1958.2, pp. 23–24.

Chin Tsu-ming, 'Che-chiang Yü-yao ch'ing-tz'u yao chih t'iao-ch'a pao-kao' (Brief Report on the Celadon Kilnsites of Yü-yao in Chekiang). *K'ao-ku hsüeh-pao* 1959.3, pp. 107–20.

BIBLIOGRAPHY

Chinese Academy of Sciences, Institute of Archaeological Research, *K'ao-ku-hsüeh Chi-ch'u* (Fundamentals of Archaeology). Peking, 1958.

Chinese Government, *Illustrated Catalogue of Chinese Government Exhibits for the International Exhibition of Chinese Art in London*, II, Porcelain. Shanghai, 1936.

David, Madeleine, 'Céramiques Song, 960–1279'. *Cahiers de la Céramique et des Arts du Feu* (Winter 1956–57), pp. 7–16.

David, Sir Percival, 'A Commentary on Ju Ware'. *Trans. OCS* 1936–37, pp. 18–69.

David, Sir Percival, 'Ju and Kuan Wares'. Introduction to the Catalogue of the Exhibition of Ju and Kuan Wares. *Trans. OCS* 1952–53.

Farley, Malcolm A., 'The White Wares of Fukien and the South China Coast'. *FECB* 7, September 1949; and 9, March 1950.

Feng Hsien-ming, 'Ho-nan Kung-hsien ku-yao-chih t'iao-ch'a chi yao' (Report on the Investigation of an Ancient Kilnsite at Kung-hsien, Honan). *Wen-wu* 1959.3, pp. 56–58.

Feng Hsien-ming, 'Lüeh t'an Wei Chin chih Wu-tai tz'u-ch'i ti chuang-shih t'e-cheng' (Brief Discussion of the Characteristics of the Decoration of Porcelain from Wei-Chin to the Five Dynasties). *Wen-wu* 1959.6, pp. 18–21.

Feng Hsien-ming, 'Tz'u-ch'i ch'ien shuo' (Brief Discussion of Porcelain). *Wen-wu* 1959.7, pp. 67–71.

Fukien Provincial Committee . . . , 'Fu-chien shen tsui-chin fa-hsien ti ku-tai yao-chih' (Ancient Kilnsites Recently Discovered in Fukien). *Wen-wu* 1959.6, pp. 62–71.

Fukien Provincial Committee . . . , 'Fu-ch'ing-hsien Tung-men shui-k'u ku yao t'iao-ch'a chien-k'uang' (Study of the Ancient Kilns at the East Gate Reservoir of Fu-ch'ing). *Wen-wu ts'an-k'ao ts'e-liao* 1958.2, pp. 34–35.

Fukien Provincial Committee . . . , 'T'ung-an-hsien Ting-ch'i shui-k'u ku tz'u yao t'iao-ch'a chi' (Report on an Ancient Kilnsite at the Ting-ch'i Reservoir in T'ung-an-hsien). *Wen-wu ts'an-k'ao ts'e-liao* 1958.2, pp. 32–33.

Garner, Sir Harry, 'Early Chinese Crackled Porcelain'. *Trans. OCS* 1959–60, pp. 19–28.

Garner, Sir Harry, *Oriental Blue and White*, London, 1954.

Gompertz, G. St. G. M., *Chinese Celadon Wares*. London, 1958.

Gompertz, G. St. G. M., 'Koryo Inlaid Celadon Ware'. *Trans. OCS* 1953–54, pp. 37–50.

Gompertz, G. St. G. M., 'Some Notes on Yüeh Ware'. *OA* (N.S.) II.1 (Spring 1956), pp. 3–8; II.3 (Autumn 1956), pp. 109–16.

Gompertz, G. St. G. M., 'The Development of Koryo Wares'. *Trans. OCS* 1950–51, pp. 11–26.

Gray, Basil, *Early Chinese Pottery and Porcelain*. London, 1953.

Gyllensvärd, Bo, *T'ang Gold and Silver*. Stockholm, 1957.

Hannover, Emil (Ed. Bernard Rackham), *Pottery and Porcelain, A Handbook for Collectors*. London, 1925.

Hansford, S. Howard, *Chinese Jade Carving*. London, 1950.

Hansford, S. Howard, *The Seligman Collection of Oriental Art*; Volume I, Chinese, Central Asian and Luristān Bronzes and Chinese Jades and Sculptures. London, 1957.

Harrisson, Tom, 'Some Ceramics Excavated in Borneo'. *Trans. OCS* 1953–54, pp. 11–31.

BIBLIOGRAPHY

Hetherington, A. L., *The Early Ceramic Wares of China*. London, 1922.

Hobson, R. L., *A Catalogue of Chinese Pottery and Porcelain in the Collection of Sir Percival David*, Bt., F.S.A. London, 1934.

Hobson, R. L., *Chinese Art, One Hundred Plates in Colour*. London, 1927.

Hobson, R. L., *The George Eumorfopoulos Collection, Catalogue of the Chinese, Corean and Persian Pottery and Porcelain*. London, Vols. I (1925), II (1926), III (1926), VII (1928).

Hobson, R. L., 'Yüeh Ware and Northern Celadon'. *Trans. OCS* 1936–37, pp. 11–17.

Hobson, R. L. and Hetherington, A. L., *The Art of the Chinese Potter, from the Han Dynasty to the End of Ming*. London, 1923.

Hobson, R. L., Rackham, Bernard and King, William, *Chinese Ceramics in Private Collections*. London, 1931.

Honey, W. B., *Corean Pottery*. London, 1947.

Honey, W. B., 'Korean Wares of the Koryo Period'. *Trans. OCS* 1946–47, pp. 9–18.

Honey, W. B., *The Ceramic Art of China and Other Countries of the Far East*. London, 1945.

Hsü Ch'ing-ch'üan, 'Fu-ch'ing Tung-chang liang ch'u Sung-tai yao chih' (Sung Period Kilnsites in the two Regions of Fu-ch'ing and Tung-chang). *Wen-wu* 1959.6, pp. 67–69.

Hsü P'eng-chang, 'Ch'üan-hsi ku-tai tz'u-ch'i t'iao-ch'a chi' (Report on Ancient Pottery Objects Found in Western Szechwan). *Wen-wu ts'an-k'ao ts'e-liao* 1958.2, pp. 38–42.

Huang Han-chieh, 'T'ung-an Sung-tai yao-chih' (A Sung Dynasty Kilnsite at T'ung-an). *Wen-wu* 1959.6, pp. 62–64.

Huang Ping-yüan, 'Fu-chien Nan-an Shih-pi shui-k'u ku yao chih shih chüeh ch'ing-k'uang' (Report of a Trial Excavation of an Ancient Kilnsite at the Shih-pi Reservoir, Nan-an, Fukien). *Wen-wu* 1957.12, pp. 53–55.

Institute of Oriental Studies, University of Hongkong, *Chinese Tomb Pottery Figures*, Catalogue of an Exhibition. With an Introductory Essay by Jao Tsung i. Hongkong, 1953.

Karlbeck, Orvar, 'Proto-Porcelain and Yüeh Ware'. *Trans. OCS* 1949–50, pp. 33–48.

Kiangsu Provincial Committee . . . , *Nan-ching Liu-ch'ao Mu Ch'u-t'u Wen-wu Hsüan-chi* (Selected Cultural Objects from Six Dynasties Tombs at Nanking). Shanghai, 1959.

Kiangsu Provincial Committee . . . , *Nan-ching Ch'u-t'u Liu-ch'ao Ch'ing-tz'u* (Six Dynasties Celadon Excavated at Nanking). Peking, 1957.

Kiangsu Provincial Committee . . . , 'Wu-tai — Wu Ta-ho wu nien mu ch'ing-li chi' (Report on a Tomb Dated 933 of the Wu Kingdom of the Five Dynasties). *Wen-wu ts'an-k'ao ts'e-liao* 1957.3, pp. 70–75, 4 pages photographs.

Kim, Chewon, and Gompertz, G. St. G. M., *The Ceramic Art of Korea*. London, 1961.

Koyama, Fujio, *Chinese Ceramics, One Hundred Selected Masterpieces from Collections in Japan, England, France, and America*. Tokyo, 1960.

Koyama, Fujio, *Shina Seiji Shi-ko* (History of Chinese Celadon). 1943.

Koyama, Fujio, *et al.*, eds., *Sekai Tōji Zenshu* (Catalogue of World Ceramics). Vols. VIII, IX, X. Tokyo, 1955.

Koyama, Fujio, tr. Daisy Lion-Goldschmidt, *Céramique ancienne de l'Asie*. Tokyo-Fribourg, 1959.

BIBLIOGRAPHY

Kuan Sung-fang, 'Chin-tai tz'u-ch'i ho Chün-yao ti wen-t'i' (The Problem of Chin Dynasty Pottery and Chün Ware). *Wen-wu ts'an-k'ao ts'e-liao* 1958.2, pp. 25–26.

Li Ch'ing-fa, 'Liao-yang Shang Wang-chia-ts'un Chin-tai pi-hua mu ch'ing-li chien-pao' (Brief Report on Tomb with Chin Dynasty Wall-paintings at Shang Wang-chia-ts'un, Liao-yang). *Wen-wu* 1959.7, pp. 60–62.

Li Wen-hsin, 'Liao tz'u chien-shu' (Survey of Liao Wares). *Wen-wu ts'an-k'ao ts'e-liao* 1958.2, pp. 10–22.

Liang Chih, 'Ting tz'u ti chuang-shih i-shu' (The Art of Decoration on Ting Porcelain). *Wen-wu* 1959.6, p. 22.

Lindberg, Gustav, 'Hsing-yao and Ting-yao; An Investigation and Description of Some Chinese T'ang and Sung White Porcelain in the Carle Kempe and Gustav Lindberg Collections'. *BMFEA* 25 (1953), pp. 19–71.

Lion-Goldschmidt, Daisy, *Les poteries et porcelaines chinoises*. Paris, 1957.

Liu Lai-ch'eng, Ni Chung-yü *et al.*, 'Kuan-t'ai yao-chih fa-chüeh pao-kao' (Report on the Excavation of the Kuan-t'ai Kilnsite). *Wen-wu* 1959.6, pp. 59–61.

Los Angeles County Museum, *Chinese Ceramics*, A Loan Exhibition. Los Angeles, 1952.

Los Angeles County Museum, *The Arts of the T'ang Dynasty*, A Loan Exhibition. Los Angeles, 1957.

Mayuyama, Junkichi, *Chinese Ceramics in the West. A Compendium of Chinese Ceramic Masterpieces in European and American Collections*. Tokyo, 1960.

National Gallery of Art, Washington, etc., *Masterpieces of Korean Art*. Washington, 1957.

Newton, Isaac, 'A Thousand Years of Potting in the Hunan Province'. *Trans. OCS* 1950–1951, pp. 27–36.

Newton, Isaac, 'Chinese Ceramic Wares from Hunan'. *FECB* X, 3-4, (September–December 1958), entire.

Newton, Isaac, 'Some Coloured and White Wares from Hunan'. *Trans. OCS* 1951–52, 1952–53, pp. 25–35.

OCS, London, *Chinese Ceramic Figures*. London, 1947.

OCS, London, *Celadon Wares*. London, 1948.

OCS, London, *Exhibition of Chinese Jades*. London, 1948.

OCS, London, *Exhibition of Monochrome Porcelain of the Ming and Manchu Dynasties*. London, 1948.

OCS, London, *Exhibition of Wares of the T'ang Dynasty*. London, 1949.

OCS, London, *Exhibition of Sung Dynasty Wares; Ting, Ying-ch'ing and Tz'u-chou*. London, 1949.

OCS, London, *Exhibition of Enamelled Polychrome Porcelain of the Manchu Dynasty, 1644–1912*. London, 1951.

OCS, London, *Exhibition of Early Chinese Bronzes*. London, 1951.

OCS, London, *Exhibition of Sung Dynasty Wares, Chün and Brown Glazes*. London, 1952.

OCS, London, *Exhibition of Ju and Kuan Wares*. London, 1952.

OCS, London, *Loan Exhibition of Pre-T'ang Wares*. London, 1953.

OCS, London, *Loan Exhibition of Chinese Blue and White Porcelain, 14th to 19th Centuries*. London, 1954.

BIBLIOGRAPHY

OCS, London, *Loan Exhibition of the Arts of the T'ang Dynasty*. London, 1955.

OCS, London, *Loan Exhibition of the Arts of the Ming Dynasty*. London, 1957.

OCS, London, *Loan Exhibition of the Arts of the Sung Dynasty*. London, 1960.

Ozaki, Nobumori, 'Chinese Literature on Ceramics: the Necessity for Correct Reading and Rational Evaluation'. *OA* (N.S.) III.1 (Spring 1957), pp. 25–27.

Palmgren, Nils, ed., *Selected Chinese Antiquities from the Collection of Gustav Adolf, Crown Prince of Sweden*. Stockholm, 1948.

Pan Ping-heng, 'Chinese Jade Carving'. *China Reconstructs*, November 1959, pp. 17–21.

Percival David Foundation of Chinese Art, *Illustrated Catalogue of Tung, Ju, Kuan, Chün, Kuang-tung and Glazed I-hsing Wares in the Percival David Foundation of Chinese Art*. London, 1953.

Plumer, James Marshall, 'Shifting Boundaries and Changing Names; a Chapter in the Study of Temmoku, the Ware of Chien'. *FECB*, XII, 1–2 (June–December 1960), pp. 1–10.

Pope, John Alexander, *Chinese Porcelains from the Ardebil Shrine*. Washington, 1956.

Royal Academy of Arts, London, *Catalogue of the International Exhibition of Chinese Art 1935–6*. Third Edition, London, 1936.

Royal Academy of Arts, London, *The Chinese Exhibition, A Commemorative Catalogue of the International Exhibition of Chinese Art, Royal Academy of Arts, November 1935–March 1936*. London, 1936.

Rücker-Embden, Oscar, *Chinesische Frühkeramik*. Leipzig, 1922.

Schüller, Arno, 'Shichangit, ein Epi-Metaleukophyr-Pyroxenit (Plagioklas-Horneblende-Jadeit) als Randfazies ehemaliger leukophyrischer Gänge in Serpentin und Gabbro'. *Bulletin of the Geological Institutions of the University of Uppsala* XL (June 1961), pp. 429–453.

Shensi Provincial Committee ..., *Yao-tz'u T'u-lu* (Notes and Illustrations of Yao Porcelain). Peking, 1956.

Sullivan, Michael, *An Introduction to Chinese Art*. London, Berkeley and Los Angeles, 1961.

Sung Po-yin, 'Lien-chiang-hsien ti liang-ko ku tz'u yao' (Two Ancient Kilnsites in Lien-chiang-hsien). *Wen-wu ts'an-k'ao ts'e-liao*, 1958.2, pp. 27–31.

Sung Po-yin, 'Pu Jen mu chung ti Sui-tai ch'ing-tz'u ch'i' (Sui Dynasty Celadon in the Tomb of Pu Jen). *Wen-wu ts'an-k'ao ts'e-liao* 1958.8, pp. 47–49.

Tregear, Mary, 'Changsha Pottery in Hongkong'. *OA* (N.S.) VII.3 (Autumn 1961), pp. 126–30.

Tseng Fan, 'Kuang-che Mao-tien Sung-tai tz'u-yao chih' (Kilnsite of the Sung Period at Mao-tien, Kuang-che). *Wen-wu ts'an-k'ao ts'e-liao* 1958.2, pp. 36–37.

T'ung Shu-yeh and Shih Hsüeh-t'ung, *Chung-kuo Tz'u-ch'i Lun-ts'ung* (Studies in the History of Chinese Ceramics). Shanghai, 1958.

Venice, City of, *Exhibition of Chinese Art* (On the Seventh Centenary of Marco Polo). Venice, 1954.

Wang Shih-lun, 'Yü-yao-yao tz'u-ch'i t'an-t'ao' (Enquiry into the Pottery of the Yü-yao Kilns). *Wen-wu ts'an-k'ao ts'e-liao* 1958.8, pp. 42–46.

BIBLIOGRAPHY

Wang Yang, 'Te-ch'ing yao t'iao-ch'a san-chi' (Some Notes on Te-ch'ing Ware). *Wen-wu* 1957.10, pp. 60–62.

Watson, William, *Ancient Chinese Bronzes*. London, 1962.

Wirgin, Jan, 'Some Notes on Liao Ceramics'. *BMFEA* 32, 1960, pp. 25–38.

Yang Pao-hsüan, 'T'ang-yin-hsien Hao-pi ku tz'u-yao i-chih' (Remains of Ancient Pottery Kilns in Hao-pi, T'ang-yin-hsien). *Wen-wu* 1956.7, pp. 36–37.

Index

INDEX

INDEX

The Plates

1a

1b

2a

2b

3a

3b

3c

4a

4b

5a

5b

5c

6a

6b

7a

7b

8a

8b

9a

9b

10a

10b

11a

11b

12a

12b

12c

13a

13b

13c

14

15

16a

16b

16c

17a

17b

18a

18b

18c

18d

19a

19b

19c

20a

20b

21a

21b

21c

21d

22a

22b

23a

23b

24a

24b

25b

25a

25c

26a

26b

26c

27a

27b

27c

27d

28a

28b

28c

29a

29b

29c

30a

30b

31a

31b

31c

32a

32b

32c

32d

33

34a

34b

35a

35b

35c

36a

36b

37a

37b

37c

37d

37e

38a

38b

39a

39b

39c

40a

40b

40c

41

42a

42b

43a

43b

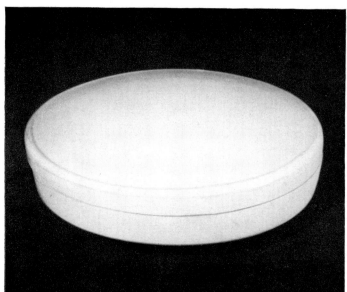

44a

44b

44c

45a

45b

46a

46b

46c

47a

47b

48a

48b

49a

49b

50a

50b

51a

51b

51c

52a

52b

52c

53a

53b

53c

54a   54b

54c

55a

55b

55c

56a

56b

57a

57b

58a

58b

59

60a

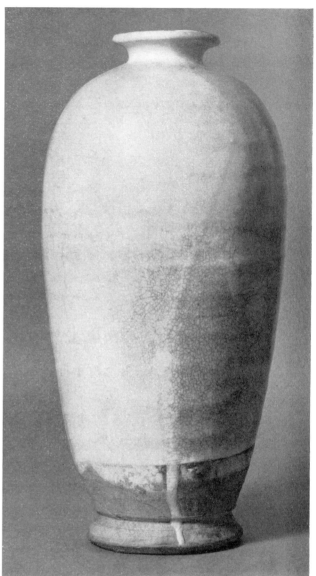

60b

60c

61a

61b

61c

62a

62b

62c

63a

63b

64a

64b

64c

65a

65b

66a

66b

66c

67a

67b

67c

68a

68b

68c

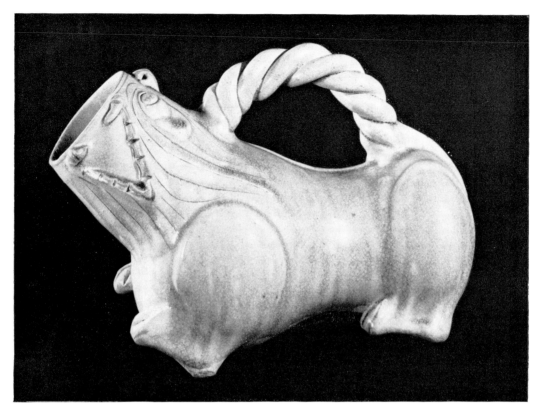

69a

69b

70a

70b

70c

71a

71b

71c

72a

72b

72c

73

74a

74b

75a

75b

76a

76b

76c

77a

77b

78a

78b

79a

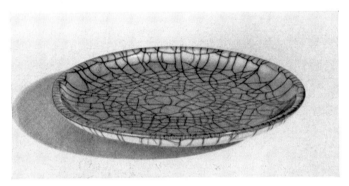

79b

79c

79d

80a

80b

81a

81b

81c

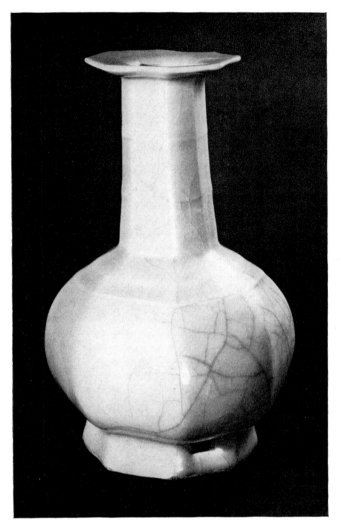

82a

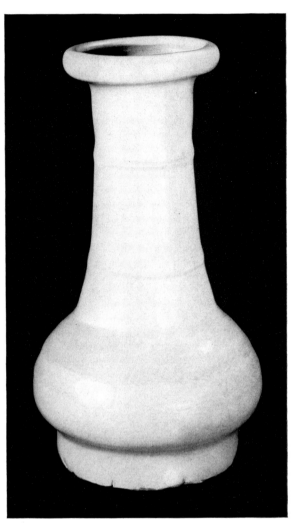

82b

82c

83a　　　　　　　　83b

83c

84a

84b

84c

85a

85b

85c

85d

86a

86b

86c

87

88a

88b

89a

89b

89c

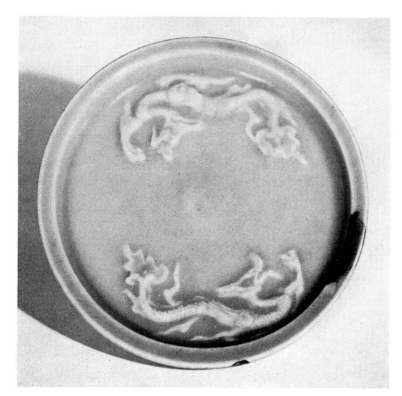

90a

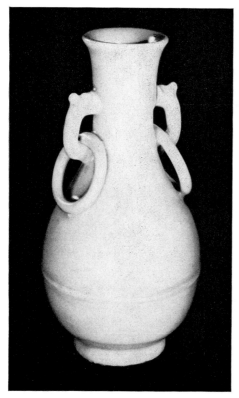

90b

90c

91a

91b

91c

91d

92a

92c

92b

92d

93a

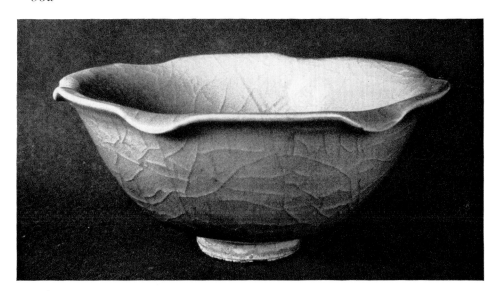

93b

93c

94a

94b

95a

95b

95c

96a 96b

96c

97a

97b

97c

98a

98b

98c

99a

99b

100a

100b

100c

101a

101b

101c

102a

102b

103a

103b

104a

104b

104c

105a

105b

105c

106a

106b

107

108a

108b

109a

109b

109c

110a

110b

111a

111b

111c

112a

112b

112c

113a

113b

113c

114a

114b

114c

115a

115b

115c

115d

116a

116b

116c

117a

117b

117c

118a

118b

118c

119a

119b

119c

120a

120b

121a

121b

121c

122a

122b

122c

123a

123b

123c

123d

124a

124b

125a

125b

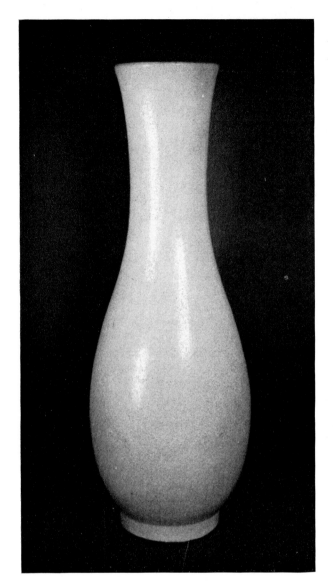

126a

126c

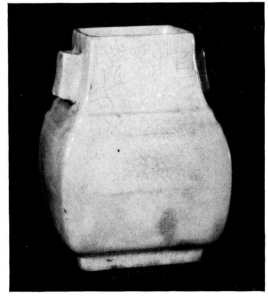

126b

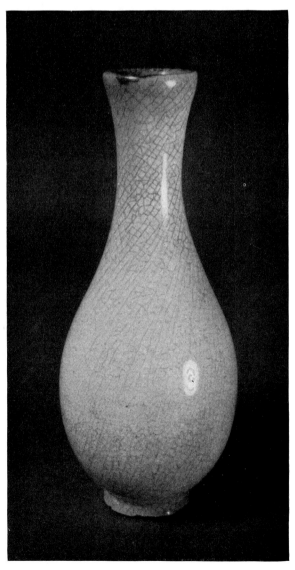

126d

127a

127b

127c

128a

128b

128c

129a

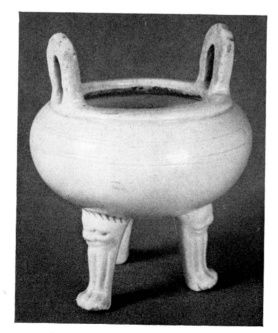

129b

130a

130b

131a

131b

132a

132b

132c

133a

133b

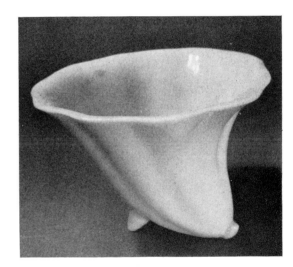

133d

133c

134a

134b

134c

134d

135a

135b

136a

136b

137a

137c

137d

137b

138a

138b

138c

138d

139a

139b

139c

140a

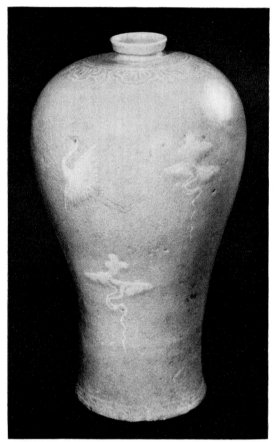

140b

140c

140d

141b

141a

141d

141c

141e

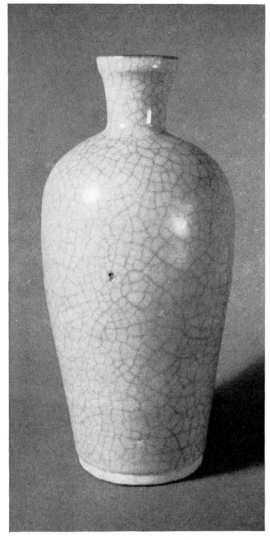

142b

142a

142c

142d

143a

143b

143c

143d

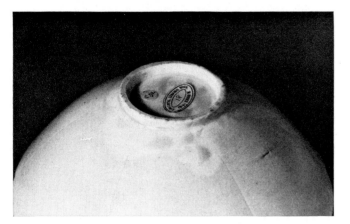

144a C. 91 (Pl. 43b)

144b C. 97 (Pl. 118a)

144c C.112 (Pl. 29a)

144d C. 211 (Pl. 44a)

144e C. 259 (Pl. 29c)

144f C. 108 (Pl. 121a)

145

146a

146b

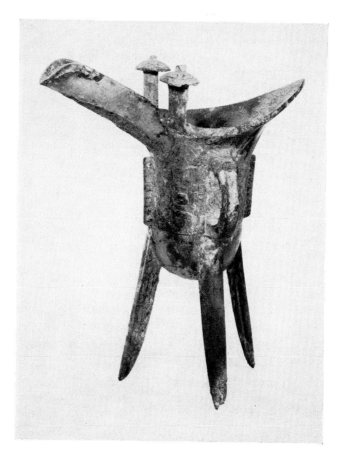

147a

147b

148a

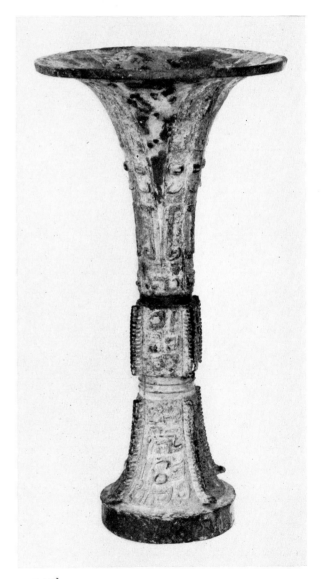

148b

149a

149b

150a

150b

151

152a

152b

153a

153b

154a

154b

154c

155a

155b

156a

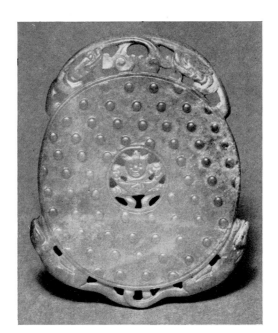

156b

157a

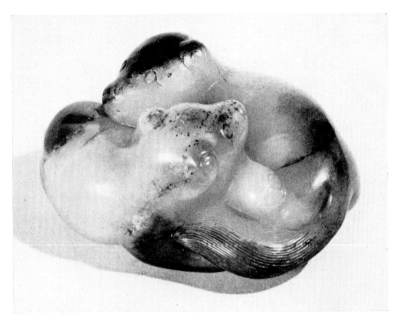

157b

157c

158a

158c

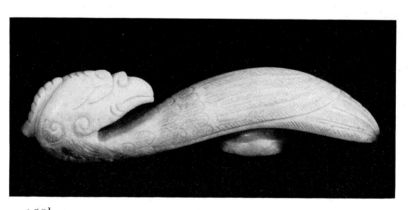

158b

159a

159b

160a

160b